Golden Trees of the

Mountain West:

A Natural History of Larch

Stephen F. Arno

Dedication

To Dr. Jim Habeck, Dr. Bob Pfister, Dr. Clint Carlson, all the members of Friends of Lolo Peak, retired USFS Ranger Tim Love, my grandson Alex Arno, who arranged the photos in the manuscript, his wife Jenny Smith who was the tireless editor, and reviewers Don Hanley, Penny Morgan, and Helen Smith.

CONTENTS

INTRODUCTION

Ever since I can recall, I have had an affinity for forests and trees. When I was young, my family lived in a semi-rural area of western Washington. My mother's diary contains a story of how I virtually raced up an Olympic National Park trail ahead of her and Dad at age two and still in diapers! When I was young, I was often missing and found wandering around among the trees, so there was never any doubt that I would choose a career in Forestry.

In 1961, I attended Olympic Junior College and took forestry and botany classes. Unlike many of my peers, I was more interested in forest ecology than timber harvesting. I did not believe that forests should remain undisturbed by humans. Instead, I have always wanted to know how forest ecosystems worked in the past and how foresters might mimic those processes today. As a student of forest ecology, I found it valuable to have these various experiences and perspectives in the field. I spent three summers as an assistant log scaler. I saw that some trees would wrap themselves around large granite rocks, which really fascinated me. As a seasonal firefighter with Washington State's Department of Natural Resources and Conservation, I learned how fire was an integral and natural part of the history and management of western forests. Humans could not simply avoid using fire for forest management. A couple summers, I worked at Sequoia-Kings Canyon National Park and Olympic National Park as a ranger-naturalist. I had an opportunity to interpret natural phenomenon for hundreds of people each season. Over time, I discovered a passion for helping people understand and connect to the natural world.

I also enjoyed writing and educating people about forest ecology and management. I was perhaps the first forestry student to take a magazine article writing class at Washington State University in Pullman, where I was finishing my bachelor's degree. With the instructor's helpful advice, I published articles in *National Park's* magazine and the Sunday edition of *The Register Guard,* a daily newspaper out of Eugene, Oregon. Early in my writing career, while at WSU, I also took a Synecology class taught by renowned ecologist Dr. Rexford Daubenmire. He was an expert in how trees and other plants interact with their environment. An aspiring writer about forest ecology, I submitted an article I wrote about this subject to him, prior to the class. He was kind enough to read my gibberish and advise me to learn about the subject before I wrote again!

I finished my Bachelor of Science degree in 1965. I was accepted for fellowship program through the University of Montana. In September 1965, my wife Bonnie and I moved to Missoula, Montana. Bonnie got a job teaching fifth and sixth grade and I pursued my masters and doctorate degrees at UM We would call Montana home for many years to come.

My Master's thesis focused on interpreting timberlines. One of the first things I did upon arriving at campus was to meet forest ecology professor, Dr. James R. Habeck, who would later aid me in my field research. My research focused on interpreting timberlines as an effort to aid park naturalists acquaint visitors with the subalpine-alpine ecotone of the Northwest. I was incredibly grateful that Jim agreed to accompany me in the field, which was unusual for professors. Together, we traveled to study timberlines in western Montana and Idaho. I found him to be invaluable, as he was a perceptive, natural historian in the manner of a David Douglas and Alexander von Humboldt.

I finished my Master's in 1966 and immediately started working on my doctorate, which was largely shaped by my experiences with alpine larch the year prior. Before classes began for my master's program (back in 1965), I hiked the strenuous circuit of Enchantment Lakes and Mount Stuart in central Washington state. I wanted to see the alpine larch that John Leiberg had vividly described in his U.S. Geological Survey in the 1899 (see his quote on page 31). Their hardiness amazed me. Upon moving to Missoula, the heart of larch county, I went in search for alpine larch in my area. I climbed Carlton Ridge near Florence, which was covered with eighteen inches of new powdery snow. The alpine larch was in full color. It was amazing how resilient these trees were, yet there was so little known about them. Standing on that ridge, I confirmed my decision to study the ecology of alpine larch as the subject of my dissertation.

By 1970, I had earned a doctorate in Forestry and Plant Science. My wife and I had our first child. I desperately needed a job, but there was a recession at the time. I got a job sorting lumber at a local mill, but I didn't reveal my educational background because it was unusual to have a college graduate working the green chain. Also, as they say, "Last one hired is the first one fired." The recession worsened, and one day at lunchtime, after only three weeks on the job, they gave me notice to not to report for work the next day.

Then, I applied for a position with the U.S. Forest Service. I was told there were only four forester positions available and that it would be very competitive. The Forest Service gave each applicant a score based on education and experience. The highest scoring applicants would be offered the position. However, there was a risk that hiring managers may chose applicants with the highest scores without checking to see what factors made up the score. My score on the hiring chart was 100, but even so, I was anxious. Competing applicants could earn five extra points for being military veterans, so another applicant could get a base score of 96, earn five points for being a veteran of the Vietnam War, which would give them a total score of 101. I was relieved when the Forest Service called me. They had funds to hire six foresters instead of just four and they asked me if I would accept a beginning forester appointment on the Kaniksu National Forest. I was so relieved I almost laughed aloud. I accepted the position and it led to a 28-year career in forest ecology research, which I have continued into retirement.

Throughout my career, I have enjoyed writing to help people gain a better understanding of our native forests as ecosystems and natural resources, and to help promote conservation and appropriate forest management. Several books have been written about ponderosa pine (*Pinus ponderosa*), Douglas-fir (*Pseudotsuga menziesii*), western red cedar (*Thuja plicata*), and a few about Sitka spruce (*Picea sitchensis*) and the western white pine (*Pinus monticola*). But no one has written about larch trees yet. I personally find Northwestern larch extraordinary and I wanted to share this interest with others, which has resulted in this book.

This book explores the ecology of larch trees and what makes them so extraordinary. The first chapter "Unlocking Larch's Secrets" focuses on what specifically makes larch unique, especially regarding their genetics and physical characteristics. The second chapter "Larch Distribution" covers specific areas where alpine and western larch live, as well as where other species of larch live in the world. The third chapter, "Northwestern Larch Uses Throughout the Ages", illustrates the different ways that humans and animals have interacted with larch throughout history. The fourth chapter, "What Future Awaits Larch?", describes various threats to alpine and western larch and ways to reduce them, as well as discussing what may be in store for the future of larch management. The conclusion encourages readers to continue to learn about larch, to engage with forest restoration efforts, and to share their interest with others. The last section of the book includes acknowledgements, a visitor's guide for seeing larch in the Northwest and the Bitterroot valley, and recommendations for further reference and research.

I was nine when I first hiked the Plain of Six Glaciers Teahouse in Banff. The route features beautiful alpine larch and the trees were no doubt just starting to leaf out. Being so young, I didn't pay much attention to them. Who would have known—many years later—that these trees would become so special to me? I'm glad to have finished this book and share about these two glorious larch tree species that highlight the Inland Northwest's Forest and its high-country.

CHAPTER ONE

Unlocking Larch's Secrets

We all watch for those amazing gold candles... in the fall, and then wait breathlessly for the appearance of the chartreuse green needles which signify our late spring season.

LOIS WYTHE

Idaho's Kinnikinic Native Plant Society

The larch (*Larix*) species are a spectacular feature of the Inland Northwest, inspiring even casual observers. In early fall, the western larch (*Larix occidentalis*) (Fig. 1), with their light green hues in spring and summer, golden color in fall, and the absence of foliage in winter, stand out amidst the somber evergreens, characteristic of northern and mountain forests. Alpine larch (*Larix lyallii*) (Fig. 2) are resilient and hardy trees, growing on high ridges where other trees cannot. These trees are found in popular Wilderness areas and National Forest campgrounds, such as North Cascades National Park, the eastern approach to Mount Rainier National Park and White Pass, Glacier National Park, Waterton Lakes National Park, and Banff National Park.

There are three types of larch in North America: western, alpine, and tamarack (*Larix laricina*) (Fig. 3). This book focuses on western and alpine larch, although it's worth noting the three Northwest larch's commonalities. People frequently refer to western larch and alpine larch as "tamarack," a name that dates to early New England Colonists, who soon became familiar with *Larix laricina*. However, *Larix larcina* is the only tree whose official common name is "tamarack." The name "tamarack" was derived from a French-Canadian translation of an Algonquin native term for the tree, which was used long before the system of scientific nomenclature was created for the genus *Larix*.

The three North American larch trees stand out as extraordinary, even amongst the remarkable genus *Larix*, which consists of ten species to occupy cold regions of the Northern Hemisphere. All three of the North America larches differ greatly in their growth forms and habitats, yet geneticists have determined that the three larches (western, alpine, tamarack) are more closely related than the seven other larch species that span Eurasia. Western and alpine larch are first cousins, and tamarack is their second cousin. Tamarack split off from the evolutionary tree before western and alpine larch differentiated into distinct species. The close ancestry of western and alpine larch species is baffling since they differ greatly from each other in many ways but are both confined to the same general region of the Inland Northwest. This anomaly in genetics intensifies when Northwestern larch species (western and alpine) are compared to the eight other *Larix* species, including tamarack.

Fig. 1 Western larch (Larix occidentalis) in Mission Mountains (Arno)

Fig. 2 Alpine larch (Larix lyallii) survives deep snow in late September (Arno)

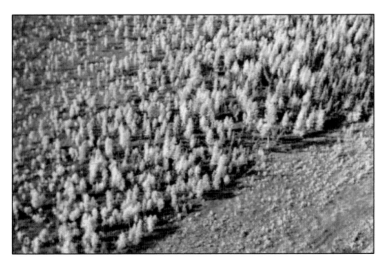

Fig. 3 Tamarack (Larix laricina) in Alberta marshland (Kevin Gedling and Stephen Mills)

Northwestern Larch

Unlike the world's eight other larch species, ours are confined to a unique region where Pacific maritime trees, shrubs, and herbs penetrate deep into the Rocky Mountains. This phenomenon of nature took ecologists a long time to decipher. Many years ago, Washington State University ecologist Rexford Daubenmire coined the term "climatic peninsula" for this inland incursion. Many other maritime trees including grand fir (*Abies grandis*), western and mountain hemlocks (*Tsuga heterophylla, Tsuga mertensiana*), as well as shrubs and herbaceous plants follow a similar pattern, but western and alpine larch are the only forest trees largely confined to the inland part of this climatic region.

The North Pacific Maritime Forest (NPMF), extending from the Pacific coast almost to the Continental Divide, is unique worldwide because it is a temperate zone forest dominated by large evergreen conifers. Other temperate zone forests, like those of the eastern U.S., consist mainly of deciduous broadleaf trees. The presence of our deciduous larch trees in part of the NPMF is an enigma.

Late in the 20th century, ecologists Richard Waring and Jerry Franklin examined research findings, climatic data, and other information to determine why the NPMF is so unusual. They found that the regional climate, which is marked by wet and cool weather in autumn, winter, and spring, followed by a warm dry summer, is largely responsible for the dominance by conifers which include our northwestern larch trees.

In contrast, temperate zone forests in the eastern United States and Eurasia have warm, wet, humid summers. Those climates favor deciduous broadleaf forests, where trees shed leaves ahead of the frigid winter and then in the spring, produce seasonal foliage designed to maximize photosynthesis. Photosynthesis is the process by which plants use sunlight to produce food and grow using carbon dioxide and water. By contrast, in our northwestern forest, broadleaved trees are at a disadvantage because the typical summer drought and low humidity stresses their fragile leaves, which require ample moisture to prevent desiccation (except in riparian areas near water courses).

Unlike deciduous broadleaved trees, the Northwest's evergreen conifers have needle-shaped, or scale-like leaves, which are protected from overheating and dehydration in summer by a small surface area coated with wax. They enter a semi-dormant state in winter but retain foliage year-round and can carry out photosynthesis during cool, moist autumn and spring seasons, and even in winter, whenever there are periods of adequate moisture and above-freezing temperatures. Many conifers are adapted to survive heavy, wet snows and sharp frosts in autumn and spring, which often cause serious damage to broadleaved trees. By having needle-like leaves and woody buds, larch trees, though deciduous, are not exposed to the vicissitudes of nature that restrict the success of broadleaved deciduous trees in most Northwestern forests. The ten world-wide species of larch are the only large group of deciduous conifers.

Most larch species can grow beyond the cold limits of evergreen conifers into the high alpine or arctic zones due to their special adaptations, including deciduous needle-like leaves and woody spur shoots that protect its buds in winter. In most alpine larch stands, the ground doesn't freeze in winter due to the insulating effect of the blanket of snow. The soil remains near 32 degrees Fahrenheit until after the snow melts in late June or July. Despite the frigid ground and deep snowpack, alpine larch trees start to produce new pollen cones, seed-bearing cones, and needles in early June, several weeks earlier in the season than neighboring evergreen conifers.

During winter, larch trees resemble a dead conifer except for the woody knobs on their bare branches. The abundant woody knobs, or "spur shoots," produce seed-bearing cones, needle clusters along branches, and growing shoots at the tip of branches and the top of the trees. At the onset of warm weather, both alpine and western larch send out new needles and growth shoots from buds which are protected in the woody knobs. Needles of western larch usually begin to emerge during April or early in May, varying by elevation. Some larch needles are dispersed along the growing shoots at the tips of the tree branches, but most radiate in clusters of 20–50 needles from the spur shoots, which protrude like warts on the branches. When the needles turn golden yellow and drop off the trees in autumn, the woody spur shoots shelter buds that will produce the next cluster of needles. The spur shoots live for many years and continue to produce new foliage every spring.

Spur shoots are useful for differentiating our two larch species from one another, as well as dead conifers, in winter. However, if you don't know to look for them, it can be easy to mistake them as a dead conifer. Many a newcomer to the Inland Northwest has felled an apparently dead tree for firewood in late fall, only to discover that it was a living, dormant western larch. Larch wood may be quite heavy (even heavier than a dead oak) because its dense wood is filled with water. A century ago, when larch logs were floated down rivers to sawmills, the butt logs would sink and therefore had to be chained to logs of other trees that are more buoyant. Despite this precaution, tens of thousands of logs sunk and have recently been retrieved and sawed into lumber.

Another extraordinary feature of our Northwestern larch trees is their ability to root in talus boulder-piles that are too deep for other species of evergreen trees. Western larch uniquely grows on boulders, bedrock, and "scree," a term for fine unstable rock that is difficult even for deer to travel through (Fig. 4). On occasion, when a rockpile in the bottom of a steep canyon where western larch grows has been excavated, it has revealed ice deep below, thus providing the trees with a source of water.

Although western larch is much more abundant than its high-mountain cousin, alpine larch is like the other larch species worldwide, in that, most of them ascend to the cold limits of trees in high mountains or the arctic and they often grow on swampy ground that few other trees tolerate. In northern Siberia, two species of larch are the only erect trees that grow in a vast swampy region atop permafrost, where the shallow waterlogged soil thaws briefly in summer.

Fig. 4 Western larch on bedrock (Arno)

How to Tell Our Larch Species Apart

Identifying the two larch species is easy once you know the differences in their shape, foliage, and growing environment. Growth forms (size and shape of a tree) of our two larch species differ greatly in response to the contrasting environments they occupy. Another easy identification feature are their two contrasting elevations. Western larch typically lives in more temperate climates while alpine larch live as high as the timberlines. The species occasionally meet at the upper limits of western larch and the lower limits of alpine larch. These locations are typically on virtually inaccessibly steep, boulder-strewn northern slopes and avalanche chutes. The best-known locations are inside shady canyons in the Bitterroot range from southwest of Lolo to Victor, Montana.

Characteristics of the Western Larch

Amongst North America's three larch species, the western larch is the most common. However, it is also the most unusual (when compared to *Larix* worldwide) due to its large size and because it does not approach either the alpine or Arctic timberlines. Western larch inhabit a temperate habitat and grows around 1,500-7,000 feet elevation. Larch trees are "shade-intolerant", which means they will not thrive in shady environments. They will be outcompeted for growing space by their shade-tolerant evergreen associates, such as fir and spruce. However, western larch has evolved strategies for persevering. New western larch trees can only become established and achieve rapid growth in places largely cleared of vegetation by events such as wildfires or logging, or in areas that have been thinned and had prescribed burns. These environments reduce the competition for space and nutrients from shade-tolerant conifers and the thick undergrowth of shrubs, grasses, and other plants.

Given the opportunity to take root in these situations, larch seedlings grow tall rapidly in height and outstrip its evergreen competitors (Fig. 5). On sites with good soil and light, western larch often attains 160 to 200 feet in height as a mature tree. If maturity is defined by a conifer reaching its maximum height, western larch achieves that in roughly 130 to 150 years. Under most conditions, alpine larch trees take more than twice that long.

Western larch trees have short, horizontal branches that start high above the ground, except in very young trees. Since its foliage is high above the ground, it is easily exposed to sunlight, which enhances the tree's photosynthesis. Its crown is narrow and cylindrical. During the growing season, western larch's foliage, and even its canopy high overhead, is visibly yellow-green and shiny. Young twigs of western larch are mostly hairless and shiny.

Bark is another distinguishing feature for the larch species. Western larch has deeply furrowed, dark purplish-brown bark, which becomes very thick as trees mature. Old western trees commonly have a layer of bark five to six inches thick near their base, insulating their sap-filled inner bark.

Fig. 5 Western larch seedling in burned soil (Arno)

If you carve off some of the outer bark of a good-sized western larch with a knife, you will find that the bark flakes look like pieces of a puzzle. This bark characteristic is special to larch, but also to mature ponderosa and Douglas-fir. The thick-bark design allows mature western larch trees to survive lethal heat generated by surface fires. This is part of what makes them fire resistant. The bark design of mature western larch trees allows them to be identified even a century after they were logged or burned.

The western larch is also more fire resistant due to its height. Their branches start high, away from ladder fuels, and are not particularly combustible. When there is a fire, trees are susceptible to crown scorch. Crown scorch occurs when heat damages foliage. Western larch has an advantage over their evergreen associates because its deciduous foliage can regenerate soon after a fire. Evergreen conifers who suffer crown scorch do not recover as easily as larch since they do not lose their foliage. A tall western larch is generally not defoliated during a fire season because its high, open crown, and deciduous foliage protect it from crown scorch.

These various characteristics make western larch the Inland Northwest's most likely tree to survive fires, a huge advantage in a region known for frequent fires.

Characteristics of the Alpine Larch

Alpine larch is abundant in our region's highest mountains. While forests of western larch turning color draws people's attention, even from miles away, many people who hike in Northwest high country don't notice alpine larch until they happen upon it in early fall. Alpine larch groves are often hidden from view inside secluded cirque basins—amphitheater shaped basins with steep walls carved by a mountain glacier, and often containing a lake or pond. These cirque habitats are found on the shady side of lofty peaks, and deep within roadless areas. Many people who notice alpine larch for the first time, wonder if it is western larch, despite its entirely different form and setting. As might be expected, considering its lofty and therefore colder habitat, alpine larch turns golden-yellow in readiness for winter dormancy in late September, about a month earlier than lower-elevation western larch.

In sharp contrast to western larch, alpine larch is slow-growing, short tree due to the severe weather and rocky conditions that it inhabits. Alpine larch often ascends into the edge of alpine tundra and steep "rock-land", beyond the upper limits of other trees. Rock-lands are slopes covered with boulders (coarse talus) and bare bedrock. On those sites, alpine larch's roots penetrate deep into the broken rock and crevices, tapping water and nutrients that allow it to grow and survive the harsh environment for hundreds of years.

Alpine larch regenerate and mature in areas where fires have cleared or reduced competition by killing the other tree species. On more competitive terrain, alpine larch's success lasts only until the competition regrows. Alpine larch trees are ultimately replaced by shade-tolerant species like subalpine fir (*Abies lasiocarpa*), spruce, and even the shade-intolerant but fast-growing lodgepole pine.

Having adapted to monumental snowfall and hurricane-force winds, alpine larch is a relatively short tree, usually 40 to 80 feet tall at maturity. Its branches are usually within reach from the ground, and it has a spreading or multi-stemmed canopy composed of long flexible branches and branchlets that hang down. Foliage of alpine larch appears bluish-green and dull. Young twigs of alpine larch are covered with fine woolly hairs all year (Fig. 6). The woolly hairs of the alpine larch are thought to be an adaptation to the cold environment in which it grows.

Fig. 6 Woolly hairs on alpine larch twig (Arno)

Studies in Alberta, Canada, found that an alpine larch takes 25 to 30 years to reach one foot in height. However, during that period, it develops an extensive root system. During that initial period, alpine larch takes on a somewhat bushy form, and often retains green lower foliage ("wintergreen") through the long winters, while losing its upper foliage (Fig. 7). After getting established, alpine larch saplings begin growing vertically at the rate of a few inches each year.

When alpine larch grows on boulder piles on northern slopes at somewhat lower elevations, alpine larch sometimes becomes a stout giant with massive limbs like an ancient oak. On the wind-blasted alpine tundra, evergreen trees are reduced to a dense shrubby form called alpine scrub (also known as krummholz), two to three feet high, that grow on the leeside of boulders (Fig. 7). The snow collects in the saddles and the exposed places, blowing across the lee side of boulders and piling up in a snow drift, nourishing the little trees that grow there. On many of these sites, alpine larch forms a shrubby cushion or skirt of low branches. It also produces a wind-shaped vertical stem with a narrow vertical strip of foliage confined to the leeward side. This feature, called a flag, juts up as much as ten feet above its cushion, defying the savage elements.

Fig. 7 Wintergreen bottom limbs of an alpine larch sapling (Arno)

In contrast to the western larch, alpine larch is not fire resistant. As alpine larch trees mature, their relatively thin bark (only about an inch thick), is smooth at first and then develops gray or brown scales separated by shallow, vertical fissures. Like many other high-elevation trees, it apparently did not evolve thick bark because it had other strategies for surviving fires, such as growing in wet sites, habitats where undergrowth is sparse and non-combustible, and in very rocky areas where surface fuel is virtually non-existent. As a result, historical fires have seldom killed many of these high-country larches, even when fires burned through the evergreen forests at lower elevations. Perhaps surprisingly, alpine larch, like its ridgetop companion whitebark pine (*Pinus albicaulis*), often benefits from fires that sweep through the subalpine forest below.

Larch Regeneration

Both species have yellow-brown pollen cones about half an inch long that develop from the specialized woody buds called spur shoots. Pollen cones are small fleshy male cones that spread yellow pollen grains far and wide in the wind and then disintegrate. Most people who live near a U.S. Western Forest are familiar with the similar, much more abundant pollen grains from pine trees. Pine pollen is as fine as dust, and it often clouds the air in the spring.

Pollen grains fertilize long-lasting, female seed-bearing cones. Most conifers, including larch, bear both male (pollen) and female (seed-bearing) cones on the same tree, but pollen is spread so widely that there is little danger of inbreeding. Inbreeding would be bad for genetic diversity. For a few weeks after the young seed cones break out of their winter quarters in spur shoots, they are reddish-purple and look like tiny ornaments on bare-appearing branches of alpine larch trees. Western larch has similar cone-lets, but they are usually located high up in tall trees and out of sight (Fig. 8).

By early September, the seed cones of alpine larch have matured, are light brown. They also have a long, narrow, papery bract projecting from between each cone scale, an unusual characteristic for conifers. Douglas-firs also have this feature, which is interesting because Douglas-fir are thought to be the closest evergreen relative of larch trees. Seed cones of western larch mature in late October. After the incipient seed cones start to emerge, then larch needle clusters and growth shoots slowly begin emerging from their own spur shoots.

Fig. 8 New male (pollen) and female (seed) cones and spur shoots (Arno)

Seed cones bear viable seeds every few years or only once in a decade in late summer. If seed cones are damaged by a hard frost, insects, fire, or other unfavorable conditions, then larch do not bear viable seeds. The mature cones of western larch average less than one and a third inches long, while those of alpine larch are somewhat longer. The cone scales of alpine larch flex open in September, while western larch cones open fully in October. After the cone scales open, larch cones release their small seeds, which have a papery wing, and can be carried a hundred yards or more in a stiff wind.

Overall, western and alpine larch are fascinating, hardy trees which add significant beauty to our Northwestern forests. Below is a table to better compare their differences.

Table 1. Differences between Western and Alpine Larch		
Characteristic	Western Larch *Larix occidentalis*	Alpine Larch *Larix lyallii*
Elevation	500 – 2,400 m (1,600 - 7,900 ft)	2,560 – 2,800 m (8,400 to 9,200 ft)
Location	Temperate	High cirque basins, boulder-clad ridges
Growing	Fast growing	Slow growing
Shape	Taller tree with horizontal limbs that start high above the ground and a big canopy	Sometimes a stout giant with massive limbs like an ancient oak. On the wind-blasted alpine tundra, trees are reduced to a dense shrubby form
Height at maturity	160-200 ft.	40-80 ft.
Foliage	Yellow-green and shiny. Turns color around October.	Bluish-green, dull. Turns color around September.
Young twigs	Hairless, shiny	Fine woolly hairs
Branches	Higher above the ground	Lower, some within reach of the ground
Cones	Yellow-brown pollen cones, half an inch long—smooth, mature in Oct.	Yellow-brown pollen cones, half an inch long –woolly in winter, mature early Sep.
Bark	Furrowed, thick dark purplish brown	Relatively thin bark (1 inch thick), gray or brown scales, shallow vertical fissures
Fire resistant	Yes	No

CHAPTER TWO

Larch Distributions

"(It) is the tree above all others… that is fashioned to withstand successfully the rigorous climatic conditions prevailing on the high and bleak summits… With light and graceful foliage, offering slight resistance to the winter's blasts, a compact strong trunk, and a root system firmly anchored in the crevices of the underlying rocks, it can bid defiance to winds of any violence…"

JOHN LEIBERG

Forest Reserves, Volume 20, Part V, p. 336

Tree distributions are fascinating for ecologists because it helps us understand the climate of an area. Ecologists can discern whether an area is favoring larch or other kinds of trees based on the number of the trees, their size and shape, and their health. Tree distributions are impacted by many factors, but namely competition for resources and climate. Western and alpine larch compete with other trees and shrubs for space, water, and nutrients. Interestingly, western and alpine larch are the only conifers that are largely restricted to the inland portion of the Pacific Northwest.

Western Larch's Predictable Distribution

Both western and alpine larch inhabit mountain country eastward from the crest of the Cascade Range, but as the maps of their distributions show, there some big differences (Fig. 9).

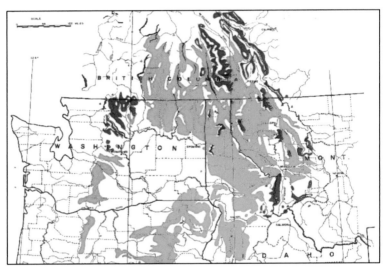

Fig. 9 Contiguous distribution of western larch (green) and broken distribution of alpine larch (purple) (Arno)

Western larch is almost exclusively restricted to the Columbia River Basin, where it is abundant on moist mountain slopes from central Oregon, as far south as Burns, to west-central Idaho as far south as Boise. This is much farther south than the range of alpine larch, but western larch doesn't spread as far north in Canada as alpine larch does.

Western larch forms beautiful forests on moist sites throughout the mountains of central and eastern Washington, northern Idaho, and northwestern Montana, but dwindles rapidly south of Victor, Montana, more than 100 miles northeast of its major distribution in central Idaho. Yet, in forest plantations thirty miles or more south of Victor, MT, it grows vigorously. A handful of isolated western larch trees stand out when they are in fall color amid the dark green conifer forest barely east of the Continental Divide in Waterton Lakes National Park, Alberta.

There are some unusual aspects of western larch's distribution. It extends west in mountains rising above the Columbia River Gorge in southwestern Washington and northwestern Oregon as far as Cascade Locks, Oregon, and Stevenson, Washington, but not as far west as 4,082-ft. Larch Mountain, a very popular day hike just east of Portland. Staff members on the Mount Hood National Forest explain that the Bridal Veil Timber Company had a sawmill on the mountain and marketed lumber from the abundant Noble fir (*Abies nobilis*) as "larch" for fifty years. The 3,480-ft. Larch Mountain to the north in Washington, almost directly across the Columbia Gorge from Oregon's Larch Mountain, is even less likely to harbor western larch, but checking that out can be left to tree sleuths.

North of Snoqualmie Pass on Interstate 90 in Washington state, western larch is largely confined to mountains 80 miles farther east than the larch in southwestern Washington—to the longitude of Chelan (about 120 degrees W.) and the Methow and Chewack Rivers in north-central Washington, as well as in southern British Columbia. Forester Don Hanley reports that there is an exceptionally nice stand of western larch at Blewett Pass in central Washington.

Another anomaly is that Montana claims the national record-size larch trees, currently at Seeley Lake. It is seven feet three inches in diameter and 163 feet tall with another ten feet of dead top. It is about 1,000 years old. There is a small parking spot and interpretive trail leading to the giant that the locals affectionately call "Gus" in the easily accessible Girard Grove (47.188N x 113.518W) (Fig. 10).

Fig.10 Record-Size western larch at Seeley Lake
(Arno)

There was a much bigger larch photographed (Fig. 11) in Wolf Valley, near Libby, Montana, that died in the mid-20th century. Since Charles Sprague Sargent's 1884 "Report on the forests of North America" report, record-size larch has been associated with northwestern Montana.

Western larch and the inland Douglas-fir are the only native conifers for which Montana holds the national records. The other northwestern conifers grow larger in the Pacific Coast states and in Idaho. Nevertheless, western larch

Fig. 11 Biggest western larch known. Photographed in Wolf Valley, Montana in the early 1900s. (U.S. Forest Service)

nearly as large as Montana's are found in northeastern Oregon and conveniently in the Pleasant Valley Campground along Washington 410, a few miles east of Mount Rainier National Park. Idaho's champion larch is also more than six feet in diameter.

Oregon's Elkhorn Mountains, home of two of the largest western larch trees, offer a 106-mile-long loop trip known as the Elkhorn Scenic Byway that threads through western larch-mixed conifer forests on moist sites before and after climbing among the Elkhorn peaks. The driving loop also passes through several ghost towns, one of the heaviest concentrations of the 1860s gold-rush historical sites in the West. The State and National Forest loop drive branches off to the west from Interstate 84 at Baker City on Oregon 7, and North Powder on Oregon 273.

The strange "larch ball" is yet another anomaly of western larch (Fig. 12). These are created in autumn when western larch's cast-off needles blow into the waters of Seeley Lake and other larch-bordered lakes. While floating in a lake, the needles become entangled into a dense sphere as big as 8 inches in diameter due to the action of the waves. Although larch balls are most associated with Seeley Lake, they are also found in some other lakes in the Inland Northwest, and tamarack larch balls are found in lakes in eastern Canada's New Brunswick province.

Fig. 12 Larch needle balls (Bev Yeltzyn and Tim Love)

Alpine Larch's Puzzling Distribution

By contrast with its cousin, alpine larch doesn't grow in Oregon, or the relatively high mountains of northeastern Washington, and has a limited presence in Idaho north of Lolo Pass, on U.S.12 east of Orofino. However, it is abundant in many high-country areas along and east of the Cascade crest north of Interstate 90 in Washington and extending into British Columbia.

It is plentiful in the vicinity of 9,416-ft. Mount Stuart (Fig. 13), the iconic crag that towers high above other mountains in the sweeping view north from the Elk Heights Rest Stop on Interstate 90 between Ellensburg and Cle Elum, Washington. From the base of the Stuart Range to the limit of erect trees, 15 different conifers, including some western larch, can be found. Alpine larch forms the limit of trees at about 7,500 feet, and it captivates the scenery in the very popular Enchantment Lakes area in the Alpine Lakes Wilderness.

Fig. 13 Mount Stuart in Washington state Cascades (Photographer unknown)

From there, northward alpine larch occupies nearly all the high mountains east of the Cascade crest. It is especially plentiful in the vicinity of Harts Pass Recreation Area (48.7205 N, 120.670 W) (Fig. 14) on the Cascade crest. Alpine larch spreads slightly over to the west side of the Cascade Divide in this area and isolated populations occur on mountains ten miles west of the Cascade crest, east of Ross Lake Reservoir in the Skagit River drainage.

Fig. 14 Alpine larch at Harts Pass in Washington state (Photographer unknown)

By far, the most mysterious occurrence of alpine larch in the North Cascades are the groves in the maritime western Cascades on the east side of the jagged Picket Range in North Cascades National Park. Climbing the ridge from Beaver Pass southward toward 8,200-ft. Mount Challenger, the first larch that comes into view is the scattered grove clinging to the steep, rocky, and nearly inaccessible northwestern face of 8,300-ft. Luna Peak (48.831 N, 121.273 W), ten miles west of Ross Lake. Then, farther south into the Picket Range, botanist Ramona

Hammerly reports having camped in an alpine larch grove, stating in a guidebook, "on the eastern edges of the Picket Range larches begin to occur." The author seems to attribute presence of alpine larch here to a rain shadow caused by high peaks to the west.

How alpine larch arrived and got established in this area is a mystery, especially since even the isolated larch groves east of Ross Lake are in the drier "rain shadow" of many high mountains, including Luna Peak, 15 to 30 miles farther west. Groves in the northeastern Picket Range may be the only place either of our two larch species cross into the west side of the high Cascades, where annual precipitation averages more than 100 inches.

Many people from western Washington drive across the North Cascades Highway (Washington 20) to recreate in the beautiful Methow Valley and the nearby lofty mountains, populated with extensive stands of alpine larch above 6,000 feet in elevation. Motorists have a rare opportunity to see stands of this reclusive species from the North Cascades Highway. In early fall, only a mile east of the Cascade Divide at Washington Pass, golden-colored alpine larch is on display directly east above the highway on the steep, east-facing slope below towering Liberty Bell Mountain (48.575 N, 120.658 N) (Fig. 15). I would recommend binoculars and visiting other viewpoints farther down the highway to fully take in this autumn spectacle.

Fig. 15 Alpine larch on Liberty Bell Mountain, North Cascades Highway
(Photographer unknown)

The Okanogan Range is a large eastern extension of the North Cascades, spanning the Washington and British Columbia border. Here in Washington's Pasayten Wilderness area and British Columbia's adjoining Cathedral Provincial Park and Protected Area, many peaks and ridges jut up above 8,000 feet. The high cirque lakes and mountains are popular hiking areas fringed with alpine larch.

Alpine larch has a bewildering distribution in the mountains farther east. About 150 miles east of the Okanogan Cascades, an isolated stand inhabits 7,260-ft. Roman Nose Peak, (48.628 N, 116. 5935 W) north of Sandpoint, Idaho, while nearby higher peaks in the Selkirk Range have none. Another puzzling population grows among the boulders atop 7,700-ft. Northwest Peak in the extreme northwest corner of Montana. This mountain is the southern outlier of British Columbia's

Purcell Range, which 50 miles farther north supports some of the most extensive stands and forests of alpine larch.

Then, 200 miles southeast of the Okanogan Cascades and south of Lolo Pass, alpine larch becomes abundant along Idaho and Montana's Bitterroot Range. Several stands of alpine larch occupy the highest peaks in the headwaters of Idaho's Selway River including 8,943-foot Salmon Mountain (44.656 N, 114.203 W), one of very few places where a large population of alpine larch is reached by Forest Road 468. This road, known as the Magruder Corridor or Nez Perce Trail Road, runs between Elk City, Idaho, and Darby, Montana, traverses Salmon Mountain at about 8,000 feet.

The route is surprisingly popular considering that most of it is a long, one-lane, tortuous route that isn't open until mid-July or later and usually closes due to snow and ice sometime in October. There are good reasons for its appeal, so people visiting the alpine larch stands on Salmon Mountain should expect to suddenly encounter oncoming vehicles. The Magruder Corridor threads through a narrow corridor within the nation's largest Wilderness complex, so its trailheads are attractive to outfitters, backpackers, hunters, and sightseers. Where the side-hill road is carved into the lower edge of alpine larch stands, a short hike up toward the historic Salmon Mountain lookout perched on top soon reveals pure stands of alpine larch in the north-facing cirque basin. On the north-facing slope below the summit, deep snowdrift sites have been colonized by dense patches of young alpine larch trees, probably because of warmer temperatures and snow melting earlier over the past century (Fig. 16).

Fig. 16 Alpine larch invading snow glade on Salmon Mountain
(Arno, 1970)

Ribbon forests dominated by alpine larch and intervening snow glade meadows are another feature seen along the trail. (Although there are reports that a wildfire may have damaged them.) These are situated perpendicular to prevailing winds which deposit a deep snowdrift on the lee side of a band of trees and the slow-melting snowdrift sites contain strips of flower-filled meadow. This process can be compared to snow fences arranged to create drifts so that they don't block a high-desert highway. The summit vista includes three similarly high peaks to the southeast that also support abundant alpine larch, but that marks the abrupt southern end of alpine larch's range, at the brink of the mile-deep upper Salmon River Canyon. The 10,000-foot mountains south across the massive gorge don't have any larch.

Visitors to Salmon Mountain are following the general route used annually by countless Nez Perce families while driving hundreds of horses through the rugged mountains to hunt teeming bison herds east of the Continental Divide in what is present-day central Montana. The Native American route was also used in the 1860s by European settlers to get from gold fields and settlements in Montana to the Territorial capitol and trade center of Lewiston, Idaho.

Alpine larch is abundant in the Anaconda-Pintler Wilderness, where it spills across the Continental Divide. The trail to Lower and Upper Carpp Lakes, south of Philipsburg, Montana, leads to beautiful scenery and many groves of alpine larch. At an altitude of 8,150 feet, Storm Lake (46.0705, 113.266W), southwest of Anaconda, is extremely popular, but marginally accessible even by high-clearance, four-wheel-drive vehicles. The last 1.5 miles, starting at the bridge over Storm Lake Creek, is best left to hiking, since the steep sidehill route has massive rocks sticking up into the road, some as much as one foot, and maneuvering through them makes it difficult for vehicles to pass each other. Whether in a vehicle or hiking this stretch, keep in mind that weekend vehicle traffic is extremely heavy.

Once at Storm Lake, a three-mile hiking trail leads along the west side of the lake and up to 9,100-ft. Goat Flat atop the Continental Divide among alpine tundra, larch stands, and sweeping vistas of 10,000-ft. peaks. Another trail heads east through "4x4 camps", areas that people camp and recreate using 4-wheel-drive vehicles, but they become very muddy over time. After you move beyond the 4x4 camp, the trail soon heads southeast 2 miles among many surprisingly healthy whitebark pines to an 8,700-foot pass. The broad, open pass overlooks the deep Twin Lakes basin and pure alpine larch stands clinging to the rocky slopes of some of the highest mountains in Montana's long section of the Continental Divide.

Alpine larch unexpectedly appears about 20 miles east of the Great Divide across the wide Big Hole Valley in two small groves atop the West Pioneer Range, while the nearby and higher East Pioneers have none. This pattern is repeated, with the species inhabiting some isolated peaks and ridges while similar or higher peaks have none. Northward, alpine larch inhabits most of the highest mountains, including those in Glacier National Park. One of the most accessible groves is located at Preston Park, in prime grizzly bear habitat, a short hike from the trailhead (48.7015 N, 113.667 W) just east of Logan Pass. The larch is easily seen—especially when in fall color—from viewpoints on peaks rising high above the east side of Waterton Lake in Waterton Lake National Park, Alberta and at the lake's south end which extends into Glacier Park, Montana.

Although western larch is plentiful in many of the lower elevation forests west of the Continental Divide in Glacier National Park, and the park has a plethora of alpine peaks, it harbors only a modest number of alpine larch trees in scattered groves. Yet, substantially lower terrain in the North Cascades and the Bitterroot Range contains extensive stands. The answer to this puzzling situation probably depends on differences in the geology. Mountains composed of granitic and quartzite rocks have the boulder-piles and bedrock that alpine larch root into well. These rock types also produce acidic parent material. Glacier Park's mountains are made up mostly of sedimentary rock—argillite and limestone—which weathers largely into shale and rocks that are alkaline, or basic. Sedimentary rock mountains generally do not support much alpine larch.

North of its isolated occurrence atop Montana's Northwest Peak, at the southern end of the Purcell Range, beyond broad intervening valleys, alpine larch makes a major appearance in the Purcell Mountains high above Kimberley, British Columbia, and in the southwestern Rocky Mountains of British Columbia and Alberta for a stretch of about 225 miles, culminating abruptly just north of Lake Louise. Alpine larch is a feature of Alberta and British Columbia (prominent especially in Kananaskis, Banff, and other provincial and national parks), however its distribution appears "spotty" on maps, merely because distribution is less documented in Canada. By comparison, the United States alpine larch distribution maps are relatively more detailed. Figure nine on page 32 details this best.

The elevational distribution of our larches relative to other forest trees is shown in Figure 17.

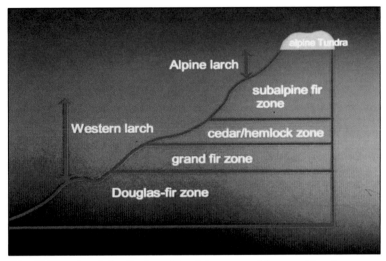

Fig. 17 Elevational distribution of larch in western Montana (Arno)

Alpine larch's erratic distribution in the Rockies is puzzling to say the least. Some of the isolated groves might be the result of its winged seeds being lofted high in the atmosphere by strong winds, seeds deposited by birds, or surviving remnants of a more extensive distribution long ago.

Larch and Avalanches

Snow avalanche chutes in high-mountain canyons provide an opportunity for both western and alpine larch to colonize sites that would otherwise be dominated by shade-tolerant trees like subalpine fir and Engelmann spruce. Because of their stronger stems and lack of winter foliage, when a deluge of winter snow wipes out trees in its path, larch trees tend to survive recurring avalanches. Western larch usually occupies the lower and middle elevations of avalanche chutes, while alpine larch inhabits the higher elevations and sometimes extends down past its usual lower limits. Occasionally the two species meet in these highly disturbed chutes. Snow creep on less-steep slopes at high-elevations pushes saplings of alpine larch, fir, and spruce over at a sharp angle, but only the needle-less larch saplings spring back uninjured when the snow melts (Fig. 18).

Fig. 18 Alpine larch and Subalpine fir in a snowslide (Arno)

On steep south-facing slopes of high peaks that are composed of big boulders, alpine larch is sometimes the only tree and is often short, stout, malformed, and ancient. One of these trees is pictured in Arno and Habeck's *Ecological Monograph*. In 1970, it was about 25 feet tall and 750 years old, nearly four and a half feet in diameter, and was kept alive by only a one-foot-wide strip of bark and living tissue. How these trees survive can be answered in part by listening. Even during

July, with no snow in sight, stream-water can be heard trickling or tumbling down beneath the boulders, and often water emerges at the base of south-facing talus slopes feeding small streams and wet meadows. One notable place this happens is at about 8,500 feet along the Trapper Peak Trail in Montana, where wet meadows are found along with a few big, spreading alpine larch.

Hybrids between western and alpine larch

Most of the world's other larch species readily hybridize, or interbreed, but it is rare for northwestern larch. The only documented area where there are a significant number of hybrids is on steep, boulder-clad north slopes between elevations of about 6,200 and 6,800 feet, hidden inside canyons of the Bitterroot Range between Lolo and Victor, Montana.

These hard-to-reach sites have normal western and alpine larch trees, a variety of larches that have a range of intermediate growth forms, and hybrids growing in the same area. Intermediate growth forms take on seemingly random characteristics of both kinds of trees due to cross-pollination. For example, some of these intermediate larch trees retain their foliage longer than typical alpine larch yet have other characteristics of western larch. Or some may have woolly twigs like alpine larch, and yet the growth form (size and shape) of western larch. Another intermediate larch tree may have shiny foliage like a western larch, but growth forms (size and shape) like alpine larch. A fully formed hybrid has more definitive characteristics because its cross pollination is more complete, or equal. Therefore, true hybrids have more balanced characteristics of both trees. True larch hybrids are typically short with drooping branches (like alpine), and have thick bark, shiny foliage, and smooth twigs (like western).

There is a single tree that appears to be a hybrid larch that grows below Doonan Peak (Fig. 19). Doonan Peak is a prominent feature on the west side of the Cabinet Mountains in the northwestern corner of Montana. The suspected hybrid lives in an open area of boulders and bedrock at an elevation of about 5,500 feet. Unfortunately, this area is now nearly inaccessible due to a dense jungle of Sitka alder and young trees that cover the abandoned road reaching it, as well as the thick alder throughout much of the forest below. The possible hybrid is about four feet in diameter and 138 feet tall, much larger than the nearby alpine larch trees. In the early fall, the tree was still green, when the adjacent alpine larch trees were golden yellow. Yet, like the alpine larch, it had a widely

Fig. 19 Suspected old hybrid larch growing amongst typical alpine larch, below Doonan Peak (Arno)

spreading canopy. In this case, a huge canopy with branches twenty-five feet long and drooping branchlets! Its canopy is completely out of character for western larch.

A search of other extensive boulder-clad slopes in the vicinity found typical western and alpine larches growing close to each other, but no suspected hybrids with intermediate characteristics. The scarcity of hybridization seems strange considering that the two species are so closely related genetically.

Tamarack Distributions

Unlike western and alpine larch, tamarack has one of the broadest distributions of any North American conifer, extending from the northeastern U.S. and Great Lakes region to Newfoundland, Labrador, and west to Alberta, British Columbia, the Yukon, and central Alaska (Fig. 20).

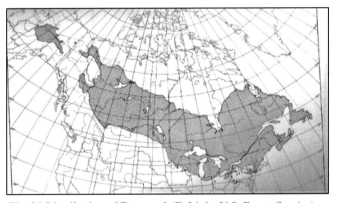

Fig. 20 Distribution of Tamarack (E. Little, U.S. Forest Service)

Tamarack is most abundant in swampy lowlands and ascends only to modest elevations in the mountains. Mixed stands of small, straight tamaracks and malformed black spruce (*Picea mariana*) characterize millions of acres of muskeg in the far north. Muskeg is a swamp or bog consisting of water and partly dead vegetation covered by a layer of sphagnum or other thick, spongy mosses. Tamarack also occupies excessively dry sites where there is scant competition for light and water from other trees.

Tamarack's southern limits in central British Columbia are separated from the northernmost western larch by more than 200 miles, and it is separated from alpine larch in Alberta by about 200 miles. Tamarack grows near the east entrance to Jasper National Park and soon becomes abundant on the highway leading Northeast to Hinton, Edson, and Edmonton.

A Glimpse at the World's Other Remarkable Larch Trees
To further show why northwestern larch are unique, here is a section to review the other larch in the world. Below is a distribution map of larch in Eurasia (Fig. 21).

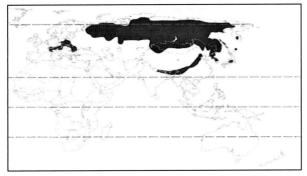

Fig. 21 Distribution of larch in Eurasia ("Conifers of the World" by James Eckenwalder)

Europe

The common European larch (*L. decidua*), like western larch, becomes a tall tree in lower and middle elevations, but like our alpine larch it also climbs steep rocky slopes near glaciers in the Swiss, French, and Italian Alps (Fig. 22). It even frames the famous Matterhorn (Fig. 23). It has long been propagated across a much larger area of central and northern Europe and grows well in some maritime regions such as at Trondheim, on Norway's central coast. Iceland, which was once virtually treeless, is now home to commercial plantations of European larch, tamarack, and Siberian larch.

Fig. 22 European larch growing in steep rocks (Photographer unknown)

Fig. 23 European larch and the Matterhorn (Photographer unknown)

Asia

Although larch trees are the only deciduous conifers adapted to frigid regions, western larch and possibly the rare Sichuan larch (*L. mastersiana*) of southern China do not reach the alpine or arctic timberlines. Sichuan larch has a small native range at the east end of the Himalayas where it reportedly grows at moderate elevations of 7,500 to 11,500 feet, but most of it has been logged by mountain people due to its high value as a construction material.

In addition to the Sichuan larch, two other larch species inhabit the Himalayas, and both reach the upper elevational limit of tree growth. The Sikkim larch (*L. griffithii*) forms pure stands in the cloud forest at about 13,000 feet elevation in Nepal and eastward to southern Tibet and southwestern China. It often occupies talus rock-land, like our alpine larch. Chinese larch (*L. potaninii*) ranges eastward from Mount Everest to southern China, where it reaches its best form at middle elevations of about 10,000 to 13,000 feet, but in some places ascends to the astounding elevation of 15,000 feet.

Japanese larch (*L. kaempferi*) is abundant in the mountains of central Honshu near Tokyo, where on good soil it grows rapidly to become a valuable timber tree. It also ascends to timberline on Mount Fuji where the harsh environment reduces it to a wind-sheared dwarf.

Russia

There are two amazing species of larch that are comparable, but even more hardy than North America's larch, that cover mountain and arctic lowland terrain across Russia. Like Antarctica, and defying comprehension, the swampy larch forest of northern Siberia receives scant precipitation (only about ten inches annually) and it is regenerated by recurrent fires during the short summers. Together Dahurian larch (*L. gmelinii*) and Siberian larch (*L. sibirica*) (Fig. 24) are mapped as one of the world's major vegetation types, comprising an area about half the size of the U.S., including Alaska.

Dahurian larch forms the only forest of erect trees in northeastern Siberia, and it occupies the coldest environment on Earth outside of Antarctica. It is an exception to alpine and arctic tree lines worldwide, which usually form where the warmest month of the year has an average temperature of 50 degrees Fahrenheit. Temperatures from several sites within the Dahurian larch forest record the warmest month as being a few degrees below 50 degrees Fahrenheit. If we had records for pure alpine larch stands that extend above all other trees on north-facing slopes, they might also reveal similar ultra-cold growing-season temperatures. Extensive pure alpine larch forests at elevations above all other trees are found on very remote 8,000-foot ridges in the Purcell Range north of Kimberly, British Columbia.

In Siberia, the Dahurian larch reaches its northern limits at about 72.4 degrees N latitude, 80 miles farther north than treeless Point Barrow, Alaska. Far to the south, Dahurian larch is a valuable timber tree, growing on good soil in mountain ranges. However, in the high arctic, it grows as a small tree atop swampland underlain by permafrost that thaws only about a foot deep in summer.

The arctic and subarctic zones of the Northern Hemisphere have been warming up faster than more southerly latitudes as demonstrated by recently opened summer shipping and tour boat routes through the Northwest Passage, north of Alaska and continental Canada. Permafrost is also thawing, which suggests that Asia's arctic larches may advance northward.

Dahurian larch spreads all the way to the eastern Pacific Ocean, including Kamchatka and the mountains of Korea. It extends south into China and to moist sites in the dry grassland plateau near Mongolia, a region named Dahuria. Although taxonomists don't agree on the scientific name, Dahurian larch is generally accepted as its common name. It merges and hybridizes with Siberian larch along a 1,500-mile zone of contact in central Siberia. From there, Siberian larch extends west into the northern part of European Russia, forming a large valuable timber tree on good soil, but also stretching north to the arctic tundra. It has long been planted for timber and habitat-enrichment in Finland and Scandinavia.

Fig. 24 Siberian Larch in Autumn (Valery Chernodedov)

Hybrid Eurasian Larch in New England

Hybrids of European and Japanese larch exhibit what is known as "hybrid vigor," namely growing faster than either of the two parent species. These larch hybrids are already propagated in about 20,000 acres of forest plantations in the northeastern U.S.

and are growing much faster than fertilized Douglas-fir. on the West Coast of the U.S. Unlike evergreen conifers, whose cast-off needles are slow to decompose and deplete soil nitrogen, larch needles, like leaves of maples and other deciduous trees, rapidly decompose to fertilize the soil. Also, despite its wide growth rings, lumber produced from hybrid larch is less likely to warp and twist than wood from fast-growing young evergreens like southern pines or Douglas-fir.

CHAPTER THREE

Northwestern Larch Uses Through the Ages

"The country was new both to Jack and to me. Huge Western Larches, my favorite among all American trees, and Western Yellow Pines and Douglas-firs made us good company."

GIFFORD PINCHOT
Breaking New Ground, p. 99

Larch has an ancient relationship with humans and animals, a variety of which we will explore in this chapter.

Native American Uses

In some valleys, such as the Jocko and Clearwater drainages around Seeley Lake, and other nearby lakes in larch forests of Montana, the Salish and allied Native American tribes evidently set fires to maintain open travel routes through the dense timber and used extensive park-like larch forests as camping areas defendable from enemy raids. The 1890s U.S. Geological Survey inspection of what was then the Lewis and Clark Forest Reserve stated in reference to the region around Seeley Lake, Montana:

> "There is no doubt that some of the fires, especially on the higher ridges, are due to lightning, but most of those

in the valley seem to have been set by Indian and other hunting parties or prospectors. The trails most frequented by Indians, as the Jocko and Pend Oreille, are noticeably burned, especially about the camping places."

Along the Jocko, Lake Pend Oreille, and other travel routes, archeologists have found numerous teepee rock rings and other artifacts of Native American use dating back several thousand years.

Alpine larch forms beautiful mixed stands with the more widely distributed whitebark pine in some high-country areas. Native Americans have had a long history of camping in these habitats while they harvested and processed the nut-like seeds of the whitebark pine. Physical evidence thousands of years old, including cup-like mortars worn into boulders and rock pestles used for grinding seeds, along with written historical accounts from settlers in the early 20th century, attest to people camping in these places over at least 3,000 years. Native American traditions, which date back untold centuries, stress the spiritual importance of these high mountain environments and a deep connection with the inspiration they provided. These traditions are described in fascinating detail on the website of the Salish Kootenai tribes of the Inland Northwest (www.csktribes.org).

The Girard Grove (Fig. 25) contains record-size larch and is probably amidst one of the largest Native American campgrounds. It has several trees with multiple fire scars, unlikely to be from lightning fires because the area is in a damp valley frost pocket. Frost pockets create a cool environment which helps limit larch competition and provided the "chilliness" required by larch.

Fig. 25 Girard Grove, underburned, at Seeley Lake (Arno)

The cross-section from one of these western larch trees have five scars from different fires between 1752 and 1859 (Fig. 26). Unlike fire-scarred ponderosa pines, fires scarred larch tends to develop heart rot, which limits the duration of their historical fire record. However, old dead larch in the area had fire scars dating back to about 1670, and groups of larch in the same age class suggest fire-initiated regeneration extending back to the early 1500s. A sample cross-section from a dead fire-scarred larch snag in the Bob Marshall Wilderness had nine fire scars from between 1687 and 1903 (Fig. 27).

Fig. 26 Cross-section of western larch with five fire scars, Seeley Lake (Arno)

Fig. 27 Cross-section of larch in Bob Marshall Wilderness with nine fire scars, 1687-1903. (Photo recovered by Robert Keane, U.S. Forest Service)

It is well-known that Native Americans set fires intentionally, often in spring before grasses and herbs emerged, and in fall, on sunny warm days (sometimes called "Indian summer") after grasses had died back, turned brown, and become flammable due to heavy frost. In both early spring and in "Indian summer", lightning fires are rare now and were likely rare then. Many fire ecologists think that the fires ignited by Native Americans made the forests more open and more often dominated by larch and pines, especially large trees, than they are today.

Misery Whips and River Pigs: Glory Days of Larch Logging

In 1883, when the transcontinental Northern Pacific railroad reached the Inland Northwest, European settler development escalated and with it came increased demand for timber to build towns, lumber mills, and roads. Several historians, including University of Wisconsin Professor Frederick Jackson Turner, declared that America's Frontier Era was over by 1891. It had been replaced by rapid development aided by railroad transportation.

Old growth western larch made tough, durable railroad crossties and was also in demand for mine timbers and construction lumber. The most efficient method of moving felled larch and other big logs to riverside sawmills was to float them down streams and rivers, a practice that already had a long history in Sweden and New England. In 1808, the famous

British-Canadian geographer David Thompson saw 200-foot-tall western larch trees growing along the Kootenai River and wrote that these trees would make good spars for ships in the Royal Navy. Less than 100 years later, the Clearwater River in Idaho, the Kootenai River in Idaho and Montana, and the big Blackfoot River in Montana, became the scene of epic log drives to transport larch and other timber to mill sites.

However, the loggers first had to fell the big larch trees using double-bitted axes and long flexible crosscut saws known as "misery whips." After determining the best direction for the tree to land, two men would work to fell the tree. They used axes to cut two notches in the trunk, above the tree butt, or basal part of the tree extending down to ground level. Oftentimes, the tree

butt is not harvestable because it is swollen, pitch-filled, or rotten, so it was important to not cut the notches too low. Into those notches they inserted springboards, about two inches thick and ten inches wide. Springboard notches can still be seen on tall century-old stumps (Fig. 28).

Fig. 28 Century-old western larch stump with springboard notches (Arno)

Standing on the springboards, and on opposite sides of the trunk, the fallers wielded razor-sharp double-bitted axes in synchrony to make a clean undercut roughly a third of the way through the trunk, facing the chosen direction of fall (Fig. 29). Then, the fallers re-positioned their springboards to the other side of the tree and began the "back-cut" with the crosscut saw that they often sharpened themselves (a difficult, and now nearly lost art).

Fig. 29 Men cutting larch on springboards (Seeley Lake Historical Museum)

Anyone who has used a crosscut saw on a fallen tree can appreciate the talent and perfect coordination required for cutting with a crosscut saw on a tree still standing. Fallers used kerosene and steel wedges to reduce binding on the saw, and hammered wedges into the back-cut to get the tree to fall in the desired direction. The back-cut stopped where there was still a "hinge" of uncut wood about three inches thick between it and the undercut. Otherwise, the immense weight of the tree might twist it off its stump and it would crash down in any direction, possibly killing a faller. It isn't clear whether fallers stayed on springboards as the tree fell. It seems jumping off the springboards would be the safest option if the boards were high above the ground. It would be rather unsafe to be on the springboards as the tree fell. The fallers would have to get away from the tree quickly after jumping, yet they may not be able to watch where the tree was falling or what was happening as they jumped. Tree trunks often bounce high after they fall.

After the tree was felled, "buckers" chopped the limbs off and sawed the trunk into logs, usually between 16 and 33 feet long. Teams of horses or oxen skidded them to a stream or riverbank, often on snow and ice-covered skid trails. Sometimes logs were skidded down steep slopes, which was hazardous for the men and animals involved, as the logs could slide down rapidly and go out of control. Great masses of logs were piled along the streams and riverbanks, ready to be dumped into fast-flowing water during spring runoff.

Once the log drive began, men called "river pigs" spent long hours, six days a week, herding the floating logs, using their agility, calk boots with sharp nails on the sole and heel, and 5-foot log rollers, called peaveys (Fig. 30) to keep their balance. River pigs also dammed tributary streams, creating large pools of water and logs called "splash dams." The loggers waited until the river was running high and fast, usually in the spring, and then released the logs into the runoff-swollen rivers. Splash dams did not make the work much easier. Logging historian Darris Flanagan notes that many river pigs could not swim! River pigs also used very long slender "pike poles" with hooks on the end to pull stray logs from eddies or the riverbank into the mainstream.

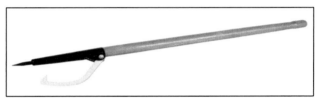

Fig. 30 Logging peavey (Photographer unknown)

The enormous masses of logs herded down streams and rivers during spring break-up were notorious for jamming and suddenly rearing up into heaps, which could throw any nearby pigs into a churning mountain of logs. Sometimes the pigs were assigned the terrifying task of breaking up a big jam in mid-river with dynamite. A deluge of rain could flood the river and propel immense quantities of logs far beyond the mills where they couldn't be retrieved, as happened in 1909 at Bonners Ferry, Idaho (Fig. 31). Untold numbers of dense, heavy larch butt logs sunk in rivers, lakes, and mill ponds (Fig. 32).

Fig. 31 Logs fill the Blackfoot River (Bonner School Library Collection)

Fig. 32 Log scaler's dismay about leaving larch long butts in Seeley Lake Area (U.S. Forest Service Archives)

Many river pigs lived in tent camps along the river, and at the end of a workday, had to hike back upstream to get to their primitive camps. If they were lucky, they stayed in a bunkhouse with wood stoves for warmth and drying out. According to Darris Flanagan, many river pigs drilled holes in the bottom of their leather boots to aid drying. He suggests that, in the early 1900s, the short life of the $18 boots was a financial burden for river men. The cookhouse, where they gobbled down sumptuous meals and coffee, was just as essential as the warm, dry sleeping quarters, where policy dictated that the lanterns were snuffed out at 9 p.m. Some mills provided floating bunkhouses and eating quarters called "wanigans" that traveled with the crew.

Starting in the 1920s, logging took on new dimensions. River drives diminished with the introduction of "steam donkeys." Steam donkeys were big, mobile steam boilers mounted on skids that used spools of heavy cable to yard logs and load them on rail cars. The steam donkeys were driven on moveable spur railroads extending into the forest. There is a refurbished operating steam donkey at Port Alberni, British Columbia. Usually, you can catch a demonstration of its operation on weekends in the summer. It is worth the trip to see this antique operate.

Along with the steam donkey, caterpillar tractors, better log-hauling trucks, and other technological innovations were developed. By the late 1940s, big, heavy, two-man chainsaws replaced crosscut saws, and by 1990, the glory days of logging old growth larch were past. Most remaining ancient larch were protected from logging and had only to contend with crowding and replacement by shade-tolerant trees and fuel buildup that potentially may lead to severe fires.

Alpine Larch Records Ancient and Future Climates

Larch tree rings, or growth rings, are very helpful in determining ancient climates and future climates of a region. The annual ring widths can indicate growing conditions. For example, a thin growth ring may suggest that particular year had poor conditions (moisture, temperature, nutrients, etc.) for growing, while a wide ring reflects more favorable conditions for growth.

The scientists who study tree rings are called dendrochronologists. To find the longest climate record in an area, they will search for the oldest trees growing on the harshest sites. Scientists can use living and dead material (snags and logs) to correlate ring widths and climate records from previous decades, and even centuries. Like ancient bristlecone pines of the Southwest that have recorded climate change for more than 5,000 years, the oldest and most climate-sensitive alpine larch and whitebark pines grow on harsh sites. However, much of the old whitebark pine population has been ravaged by the blister rust, accidentally introduced from Europe, in combination with native bark beetles. As a result, climatologists now focus on the tree-ring records from alpine larch, which extend back 800 years or more in some areas and continue to record the effects of modern and future climate.

In the Inland Northwest and northern Rocky Mountains, scientists have found that tree rings of the oldest alpine larch and whitebark pines provide the most detailed picture of climatic change. There was a study published in 2008 by Kurt F. Kipfmueller which used alpine larch growth-ring sequences to develop a 748-year chronology. This, and other studies, have found alpine larch growth rings sensitive to climatic changes, such as change in temperatures, moisture, nutrients, and diminishing competition from evergreen conifers. The New York Times has a wonderful article called "Chronicles of the Rings: What Trees Tell Us." This article is one of the most thorough and understandable explanations of tree-ring research.

The annual rings of trees that are growing on moraines and fossil timberlines are very useful for interpreting past climate. Studying larch tree rings help us understand more about moraines and fossil timberlines, and vice versa. By studying their ecology, we now understand different natural phenomena. Over the past 100 years or so, warmer periods have allowed alpine larch to colonize former summer snow-drift sites (Fig. 33) and to become established on the moraines of retreating glaciers. This latter phenomenon is seen from the views immediately below the Plane of Six Glaciers Teahouse on the enormously popular hiking trail high above Banff National Park's Lake Louise.

Fig. 33 Alpine larch invading snow glade on Salmon Mountain (Arno)

Also, near Lake Louise, the paved road to Moraine Lake and from there the trail to Larch Valley and beyond passes through the "fossil timberline" where remnants of an extinct larch forest lie amidst young larch that are reclaiming lost ground (Fig. 34). A fossil larch, probably of this species, dating from between 1000 and 1250 A.D. was found near the Athabasca Glacier (Columbia Icefield) in Banff National Park (Fig. 35) about 50 miles northwest of any alpine larch trees today.

Fig. 34 "Fossil timberline" of alpine larch in Larch Valley, Banff. (Arno)

Fig. 35 Alpine Larch Valley, north of Moraine Lake in Banff. (Arno)

Western Larch's Outstanding Wood

Western larch has the densest wood among western conifers. According to The Wood Database, western larch is one of the hardest "softwoods" in the United States.

Western larch is very resistant to decay and moderately durable. Its building strength is high, so much so that it is rated and sold as premium lumber for construction (Fig. 36). It makes beautiful flooring and window frames, but is also made into veneer, plywood, paper, particleboard, glue-laminate beams, construction, lumber, and flooring. Western larch's harvestable age, if it is on a good site, is about 80 years. On a poor site, that is, with little moisture and high temperatures or drought, it would take longer for it to grow to a harvestable age.

It also makes superb firewood because of its straight grain and high density which renders it easy to split and gives it a high heat content, so it burns for many hours in a wood stove. In a fireplace or campfire larch may throw sparks and make loud pops. You can learn more about western larch wood properties at The Wood Database website.

Fig. 36 Western larch construction lumber
(Photographer unknown)

Medicinal

Western larch also produces a unique gum, called arabinogalactan, which was reportedly used by Native Americans for several purposes, including medicinal. Some people believe arabinogalactan improves a person's immunity to various diseases.

Naturopathic doctors and some other physicians recommend it to enhance immunity to certain cancers and other diseases. For example, some naturopaths use arabinogalactan for alleviating symptoms of the common cold, flu (including the swine flu (H1N1)), ear infections, and HIV/AIDS.

In some cases, it is even used to treat liver cancer and a brain condition caused by liver damage. Larex Corporation of Saint Paul, Minnesota, has been marketing an extract of larch gum as a prebiotic fiber that aids digestion. Thorne Corporation also promotes larch as a water-soluble prebiotic, that helps control blood sugar and digestive regularity.

Arabinogalactan has not been approved by the U.S. Food and Drug Administration for prevention or treatment of diseases, but it is always interesting to see the different uses of larch, its applications, and relationship to humans.

Larch Snags: A Boon for Wildlife

Dead standing trees are called snags. A "living snag" is a tree whose core has rotted, yet is still alive, since its root system and inner bark is functioning. Even though the core is rotten, the tree may continue to live for many years because of its inner bark is alive. The inner bark of larch trees is akin to a layer of felt saturated with

Fig. 37 Living snags at Seeley Lake (Nathan Arno)

sap. This layer is very different from sticky pitch, which is used by a tree, particularly pines, to heal wounds or flood out bark beetles. Beneath the inner bark, there is a thin cambium layer, which is the growth tissue for trees, controlling growth of trees. Western larch typically become living snags due to the fungus *Phellinus pini*, which rots the core of the tree.

Due to western larch's large size and because it occupies low to mid-elevation forests, western larch "living" snags are considered the best of all habitats for hole-nesting birds and mammals (Fig. 37). The fungus *Phellinus pini* causes the core of the tree to rot, which is then easily excavated by animals, usually woodpeckers. Woodpeckers hammer out nesting cavities, and later a variety of other birds and small mammals adopt and improve these cubbyholes.

Eventually the larch snag may develop into a virtual apartment house with multiple nesting sites and a variety of occupants. Prior to and during the nesting season, living snags hum with activity as various birds pound away to upgrade their hide-away, fledglings chirp inside the nest, and adult birds scold loudly to ward off an intruding squirrel that might raid the nest. There is a constant coming and going of parent birds bringing food to insatiable chicks, who sometimes beg loudly with their head protruding from the entrance hole. Exceptionally large alpine larch snags fulfill a similar role for nesting woodpeckers, mountain bluebirds, among others. Although fewer species of cavity nesters live in the high-country due to the short summer season, limiting the time for nesting and rearing chicks as well as hampering growth of food sources.

Larch "living snags" are special because these trees may stay alive longer than other kinds of living snags– even for a few centuries! Even after the trees die, the shells may stand for a half-century, and when they fall, their hollow cores continue to provide habitat for small nesting creatures. There is a thousand-year-old snag which I have included directions to on page 106.

Bears, deer, and elk relish young larch

In the spring, both black and grizzly bears congregate in northwestern Montana forests to feed on young larch trees, often girdling them. Grizzlies hang around the Chrisman/Wiley house during spring, mostly at night. The Chrisman/Wiley Family Forest sits on the North Fork of the Flathead River in Montana. Allen Chrisman described his family's experience with bears girdling trees with me, indicated by italics:

Bears girdle up to about twenty trees per year on our North Fork [Flathead River] property, [although] it has dropped off in recent years. The girdling occurs in the spring, usually in June, when the sap is running in the conifers and the bark slips easily. The bears bite the bark near the ground level, then rip up with the bark gripped tightly in their teeth. The bears seem to prefer the small sawlog-sized western larch in the eight-to-twelve-inch diameter class. I believe it is a learned behavior passed down from the female to her young.

According to a neighbor who witnessed the event in his cabin yard, a bear can completely girdle a tree in a few minutes, by working systematically around the trunk of the tree. The bark is typically stripped off for some four to six feet from the ground up. Often, the bear does not girdle the entire circumference of the tree, thus, the tree can survive with a significant wound. Western larch trees that have been damaged by girdling are the first to start to turn color in the late summer and fall, and therefore, are easily identified. The bears seem to particularly favor larch, which grow faster and therefore have more cambium.

We have had incidental numbers of lodgepole pine and Engelmann spruce girdled. Douglas-fir and subalpine fir have not been used, based on our observations. Of course, it seems like western larch in thinned stands, with increased growth rates and therefore thicker cambium, are preferred to larch stems in un-thinned stands.

What can one do to combat tree-girdling? Allen shares: *My objective has been to grow more western larch in our mixed conifer forest than the bears can kill, and so far, it is working.*

Other landowners in the same region have also sustained bear-stripping of their young larch. Bear stripping of larch is reported by foresters in northern Idaho and northeastern Washington; however, this situation has not been observed on the east slope of the Washington Cascade Range. Video cameras have photographed bears scratching their backs, mostly against small lodgepole pine trees. In his book *A Naturalist in Alaska*, pioneer biologist Adolph Murie reported that sometimes grizzlies rubbed their backs against telephone poles in the tree-less tundra.

Deer and elk also favor young western larch trees, but not to eat them. On our Arno Family Forest above the Bitterroot Valley in Montana, and probably almost anywhere in larch country, buck deer and bull elk select larch saplings up to five-

or-six inches in diameter for scraping their antlers, apparently "polishing" them during the rut, or mating season. We and some other landowners' erect cages around saplings to prevent them from being thoroughly thrashed.

A Rich History

Overall, northwestern larch has a rich history to people, animals, and its environment. They have been used for shelter, firewood, lumber, and medicinal purposes by humans. Western and alpine "living snags" serve as a great shelter for many small-nesting mammals and birds, as well as begrudging meals for larger animals like bears, deer, and elk. If humans continue to nurture northwestern larch forests, the forests will surely benefit. Unfortunately, however, there are many threats to northwestern larch populations, some of which will be explored in the next chapter.

CHAPTER FOUR

What Future Awaits the Larch?

"There is no clearer lesson in history than that men and nations underwrite their own destruction as they violate the…laws of nature-and uniquely use and waste basic resources…The war is raging still, and it is yet very far from being won."

LEE METCALF, 1961

The threats to western and alpine larch vary, due to location and ecology. Most of the threats discussed are influenced by humans, for better or worse. However, more thoughtful decisions around forest management can help reduce the threats and consequences of fewer larch in our northwestern forests.

Threats to Western Larch and Work to Reduce Them

Arguably the greatest threat to western larch survival is fire suppression. Regular intervals of low to moderately intense fires are quite essential for natural forest management. However, in 1910, severe fires (called "The Big Blowup") spread through Idaho, Montana, and Washington, burning three million acres in only two days. The devastating fires had a formative impact on the U.S. Forest Service, which had been created just five years prior. In the next few decades, the U.S. Forest Service would adopt and implement a total fire suppression policy. The two goals of the policy were to prevent fire and suppress fires as quickly as possible once one started.

Understandably, the public was generally supportive of fire suppression. There are many reasons, but in general, people are supportive of fire suppression because fires pose a risk to scenery, profit, people, and property. People want to preserve the beauty of national forests, and some believe that fire suppression will prevent such devastating fires from happening again in the future. Furthermore, wildland fires devastate acres of harvestable timber. Even though light burning is generally good for land conditions, fires are seen as harmful to the timber industry. Finally, a major reason for fire suppression is because wildland urban interface is expanding. Housing, property, and other development in or near larch forests have made suppressing fire a high priority (Fig. 38).

European settlers were attracted to old growth western larch forests throughout the Inland Northwest as an important source of lumber. They camped and built cabins among the big larch trees adjacent to rivers or lakes. Early in the 20th century, the Federal agencies, including what later became Glacier National Park, granted long-term leases to private parties who then built highly coveted summer cabins, resorts, and church camps that continue to serve as summer retreats. Some states granted similar leases. Private timberland owners have continually sold lots and parcels of larch forest land, especially those bordering rivers and lakes. Recently most large timber companies have morphed into Real-Estate Investment Trusts (REITs) that make a business of selling off such properties. The more people who move into the forest, the more forest suppression is required.

*Fig. 38 **Home in a larch forest*** (Photographer unknown)

Fire suppression was meant to be proactive protection of northwestern forests, but unfortunately, it is largely responsible for creating the great wildfires we see today. Historically, fires naturally occurred in northwest forests every twenty to thirty years and helped manage the growth of forests and promote healthier growing conditions for trees. These naturally occurring forest fires helped prevent forests from becoming overcrowded. Fires burn through weaker and smaller trees, returning nutrients into the ground and provide more space for stronger trees to grow and mature. Trees like western larch and ponderosa pine become weakened when there is too much competition and do not receive enough nutrients and soil moisture (water) to become healthy and mature.

Overcrowded forests also allow parasitic plants and destructive insects to proliferate out of control. Since the trees grow so close together, and may be already weakened due to overcrowding, parasitic plants and insects spread quickly in an overcrowded forest. Plants like dwarf mistletoe, fungi such as needle blight and needle cast, and insects like case-bearer, damage foliage and weaken the trees. Luckily, since larch is deciduous, larch can grow a new crop of foliage even within the same year of being it is defoliated. However, the threat to the trees is still significant. Consider dwarf mistletoe, which penetrates tree branches and growing shoots and robs the tree of nutrients. Bad infections of dwarf mistletoe appear as "witch's brooms" among the live branches. Not all conifers are susceptible to dwarf mistletoe, but larch and ponderosa are highly susceptible. Fire prevents overcrowding, which slows down the spread of these kinds of parasitic plants and destructive insects.

Frequent fire also helps temper how wildfires spread and develop. When there is a lack of fire, the forest easily becomes overgrown with excess brush, shrubs, and smaller trees. These types of vegetation, which sometimes grow to moderate height, are considered "ladder fuels". Ladder fuels describe vegetation that carries or spreads fire from the bottom of the forest floor up to the forest canopy. When the forest is overcrowded, fire can easily spread from a taller bush or shrub to the lower limbs of trees, and then continue to spread up the tree and spread to other near trees. Many historically larch-dominated forests and riparian corridors with fire scars from long ago, now have dead or dying old-growth larch amidst impenetrable thickets of shade tolerant trees and shrubs. This excess of dead and alive trees, brush, and shrubs means there is more fuel to burn, so fires will get hotter.

Forest fires in the northwest spread so quickly and intensely simply because there is so much excess fuel. In the past, large forest fires were rare and often did not occur in the same area. Starting in the 1960s, however, wildfires in the Northwest became known to be large, uncontrollable, and occurring everywhere. Simply, fire suppression has enabled an excess of forest growth. Due to the Wilderness Act of 1964, which encourages fire suppression, the U.S. Forest Service is not allowed to perform prescribed management burns, which would help remove some of the extra fuel in forests and therefore lessen the severity of forest fires.

Fire suppression led to a decline of western larch in all age classes. Now the problem is not the lack of fire, but severity of fires. Western larch relies on fires to regenerate and thin out evergreen conifer competitors. A 1991 study found that fires in the North Fork Flathead River Valley, prior to fire suppression, were frequent and of low to moderate intensity. The impact of the fires produced a complex mosaic of tree stands of different ages in the predominantly western larch-lodgepole pine forest. Fire allowed many mature larch trees to survive and regenerate, while most of the lodgepole pines were killed. In a burned forest, larch seedlings outgrow lodgepole and apparently all other species native to the Inland Northwest.

U.S. Geological Forest inspector H. B. Ayres photographed a larch-lodgepole forest that had burned a couple of decades prior, showing some larch survivors along with light-colored pyramid-shaped larch reproduction and smaller, dark lodgepole pine regeneration (Fig. 39). There were no survivors of the bigger lodgepoles, but they were able to regenerate from seeds in their closed cones.

Intense wildfires now kill larch trees over broad areas, which removes the seed source. Although the fires kill evergreen conifers as well, they are so abundant

Fig. 39 Photo of western larch survivors after a fire, as well as larch regeneration 15-20 years later. Larch regeneration is light-shaded pyramids; young lodgepole pine is dark. (A.B. Ayres, U.S. Geological survey, 1899)

that they regenerate after fire. Wetter areas southward in Glacier National Park, including the Apgar Mountains and the Lake McDonald and Middle Fork Flathead Drainages, historically had more severe fires, but even in these areas, a trend toward larger fires seems to have intensified due to fire exclusion and accumulation of forest fuels.

When there is a loss of natural forest, there comes a risk of losing tree species and diminished populations, as well as larger mature trees. Younger trees can regenerate easily or be replanted, but the larger mature trees that serve as wildlife habitat cannot be replaced very easily. For example, the giant sequoia in California was thought to be fire-proof, but in recent years, more than a thousand of them have been killed by fire, insects, and disease. Firefighters have suppressed close to 99 percent of fires, including all of those that used to burn at lower intensities and favor larch survival. Fire suppression in Glacier National Park and the Bob Marshall Wilderness on the South Fork of the Flathead River has greatly increased the threat of killing all the western larch in the area.

More wildfires also result in a loss of scenery, which is a great consequence for those who use and enjoy the forests. The consequences for the natural world may be even greater. Larch, ponderosa, and black cottonwood are considered the most important species of hole-nesting birds and small mammals. A decline in these trees due to annual, intense fires will result in habitat reduction for these types of animals.

There are some efforts to reduce the threat to western larch through forest management and restoration. These tend to be primarily prescribed burns and selective cutting to remove excess fuel, which strengthen larch by removing unhealthy, diseased, or insect-infected trees. The National Park Service is conducting prescribed burning and cutting invading trees, like young Douglas-fir, in some of the prairies of the North Fork Valley to try to remove extra fuel in the area so that the fires do not get as intense. They are hoping to mimic naturally occurring fires of the past in the ponderosa pine forests and prairies. In the South Fork Valley, the U.S. Forest Service has been limited in its ability to help western larch because the agency is not allowed to do prescribed burns, nor plant new trees, due to the Wilderness Act of 1964. Since progress for forest restoration progress in the prairies is minimal, in time, the western larch will most likely disappear from these larger areas.

However, the U.S. Forest Service, Bureau of Land Management, and private landowners, have had successful attempts at restoring western larch in some commercial forests. Road access makes it easier for planting crews and nursery stock to get western larch seedlings to those locations. The western larch seedlings are planted when they are about a foot high. These sites are great for western larch because they are shielded from the sun and wind and have enough moisture. Too much sun causes desiccation. Western larch is a prime timber, species, and is aesthetically pleasing, and important to wildlife.

Despite environmental and visual harm of mid-20th century logging, it often resulted in a legacy of healthy young western larch. By the 1990s, logging was greatly reduced on federal forest lands. However, recently, forest restoration treatments that open crowded stands and use of prescribed fire have been expanded. Logging operations that reduce the density of trees and favor larch seedlings, followed by a broadcast burn to bare mineral soil, can allow larch to reseed naturally. After more than twenty years of these treatments, patches of fast-growing western larch saplings now appear in burned areas along Montana 83 state highway, northward for several miles from Seeley Lake. This area had not been able to produce successful offspring for a century.

Finally, another effort to reduce the threat to western larch is focused on educating home and landowners who live near western larch-dominated forests and who have property at risk of burning in wildfires. Naturally, not all home or landowners know the risk of purchasing a home close or in a forested area. Fortunately, there are opportunities to be educated. Nowadays, home and landowners may request a state service forester from the Department of Natural Resources and Conservation (DNRC) to visit their home or property and reduce the wildfire threat. Recommendations include cleaning pine needles out of gutters and pruning trees that are within fifteen feet of the home, removing thickets or dead shrubs and juniper bushes around the home, and in general, removing any combustible material that is close to the house (such as wooden decks, firewood, or lumber). A home that is clear of these kinds of excess fuel has a decreased threat. However, overall, the threats to western larch are certainly daunting.

Threats to Alpine Larch and Work to Reduce Them

There are several threats to alpine larch and unfortunately little effort to reduce them. It seems plausible to assume that human presence has had no effect on alpine larch, especially since they grow in remote areas. However, large numbers of visitors are attracted to alpine larch groves in high-country meadows and near cirque lakes among mountain peaks. Trout were stocked in formerly barren lakes during the post-World War II era, drawing hundreds of hiking parties as well as dozens of horseback groups, both of which trample the wet meadows and lakeshores where alpine larch grows.

One way that this threat can be reduced is to require camping permits. For example, in some of the heavily impacted alpine larch habitats, such as the Enchantment Lakes high above Leavenworth in the Washington Cascades, the U.S. Forest Service requires day-use and camping permits, which are in high demand and must be applied for far in advance of any trip. Visitors are not allowed to build campfires, and camping is restricted to designated sites away from lake shores and meadows. It is difficult to tell if the restrictions sufficiently protect the larch. Enforcing these regulations is a challenge, especially considering the reduced funds available to hire staff to monitor them, because more than half of the U.S. Forest Service budget is spent fighting wildfires. Their budget remains small, and in some years, shrinks even more. Some Montana and Idaho areas are not regulated at all.

Climatic change brings another, more widespread threat to alpine larch, a tree that requires a cold microclimate and ample moisture. Earlier snowmelt and summer drying have also influenced unusual wildfires. For example, the 2017 Lolo Peak Fire in Montana killed most alpine larch trees in what was considered the largest, nearly pure alpine larch forest in the U.S. The fire also killed nearly all the western x alpine larch hybrids growing below. Fire scar records from old-growth western larch that surround the area where the hybrids were growing, as well as on isolated old-growth whitebark pines high up on the burned ridge, show no precedent for a fire like this. The Lolo Peak fire swept upward through a vast area of extremely crowded subalpine fir and lodgepole pine forest teeming with dead trees, including dead whitebark pines, very old alpine larch, and downfall (Fig. 40). Unfortunately, climatic change is inevitable and there is little that humans can do to improve the situation. Increasingly warm temperatures will most likely reduce alpine larch populations, as the warmer weather affects their growth and ability to regenerate.

Another threat to alpine larch is when it grows in the same location as evergreen conifers. Evergreen conifer forest fires burn very hot and will burn alpine larch alongside with them. The forest that grows back in the area will be the evergreen conifers; hardly any alpine larch will grow back. Unfortunately, it is a natural and frequent occurrence for alpine larch grow in similar areas as evergreen conifer, so risk is quite high and there is little effort to prevent this threat.

While there are many threats to alpine larch and little work to reduce them, the bright spot is that it will most likely take many years for alpine larch for the populations to become smaller. This is largely since many of them grow in rocky areas, there is often a lack of fuels around them, which provides better insurance against severe fire.

Fig. 40 Surviving alpine larch after 2017 megafire on Carlton Ridge, Florence, Montana (Steve Shelly, U. S. Forest Service)

Forest Restoration Champions

Throughout my career, I have noticed that lack of public interest in maintaining the forests has led to sad consequences, including reduced funding to maintain that forest legacy. Reasons vary, but funding is impacted by public interest, lack of priority from the government (both federal and state), and other serious events, like a natural disaster or pandemic.

The DNRC, Forest Service, and local fire districts need a substantial budget to continue work in forest restoration, fuels management, and keeping the wildland interface safe from extreme wildfires. When there is a fire, a lot of taxpayer money is spent to protect individual homes, such as setting up a sprinkler system around homes with pumps, spraying down vegetation, or piling and burning small trees to reduce fuels around the homes. Currently, the Forest Service is spending more than half of its budget on fire. In 1990, the Forest Service spent around 20 per cent on fire. Wildland firefighters fire will protect homes, whether there is budget or not, but it leaves little money for controlling the wildfire itself, much less other preventative wildfire activities, such as thinning trees, removing excess fuels, conducting prescribed burns or fire to favor western larch. There were one thousand houses per year that burned down, in the West alone.

There is some hope for forest restoration. Larch, ponderosa, western white pine, and whitebark pine are high priority to be restored. These types of activities are carried out by the federal government, state governments, and volunteers. Foresters throughout the Inland Northwest are restoring stands of Douglas-fir that are infested with large areas of root rots. Western larch is by far the best species to plant because of its high tolerance to the root diseases. Western larch seedlings and other species prioritized for restoration are grown in a state forest nursery. The State charges private landowners for seedlings, or in some cases, the federal or state has budget to provide those species. Some local groups also grow seedlings for forest restoration, such as the Whitebark Pine Ecosystem Foundation, an organization who encourages volunteers to help with restoration efforts. Seedlings must be planted in a site that is properly prepared, which means scarified by bulldozer or mineral soil exposed by prescribed burning (Fig. 41).

Fig. 41 Western larch shelterwood cut and scarified for regeneration (Arno)

Forest restoration efforts are primarily funded by the federal and state government, private/local entities, and conservation groups. The trend for forest management will be to continue restoration, but progress is dependent on funding. If funds are low, there are many local organizations who raise money for forest management efforts. Five Valleys Land Trust and Bitterroot Land Trust are local organizations in my area that often raise funds through banquets and fundraisers. This money is used to do some of the preventative work necessary to keep wildlands safer.

Many more political leaders are advocating ecology-based forestry that restores fire-dependent species like western larch, and ultimately would help prevent extremely intense wildfires from destroying western and alpine larch. It is no accident that some trees survived the 2017 Lolo Peak Fire. The Stevensville District has conducted fuels management including burning repeatedly on some mountain slopes. One of their objectives was improving wildlife habitat with selective logging, thinning, and prescribed fire to promote resurgence of the aspen groves and willows along the lower slopes. Another objective was to prevent destructive wildfires, and it worked with the Lolo Peak Fire. The district had removed many of the ponderosa pines and Douglas-fir trees, finishing the project in 2016. At first, many people objected to removing so many of the large second-growth pines that were clearly marked for all to see. In time, after project was finished, nearly everyone was glad it had been done, because the Lolo Peak Fire was heading south and when it reached the ridge where it was controlled.

As for political champions, I hesitate to mention any contemporary political leaders, as agendas and perspective change over time. However, one political champion I would like to mention is Lee Metcalf (1911-1978), a former member of the U.S. Senate. Perhaps better known by Bitterroot locals for the Lee Metcalf National Wildlife Refuge, he was committed to conservation. Former senator Jennings Randolph of West Virginia described Metcalf as "a tireless champion of preserving and protecting our National natural heritage for succeeding generations to use and enjoy. This gentle man from Montana loved the Earth and all its living creatures."

In general, Congress and individual State governments have been collaborating to restore fire-adapted forests under the Good Neighbor Authority Act, which allows state forestry agencies (e.g., state governments; extension forestry; resource, conservation, and development entities) to aid federal land management agencies in planning and implementing important forest management projects, generally involving a few thousand acres. The Good Neighbor Authority Act funding is critical because federal agency fire crews can only use a limited amount of their funding for fuels reduction and prescribed burning.

Others working towards forest restoration includes a few dozen citizen-led coalitions and conservation groups including The Nature Conservancy and the Wilderness Society. These groups advocate for increased funding for forest restoration. Progress is typically measured by the amount of area that experiences forest restoration, year after year. To view progress, consider checking websites of The Nature Conservancy's Restoring America's Forests Program, the Blackfoot Challenges' Forestry Committee, and the Northeast Washington Landscape Restoration Project.

Nowadays, there are also programs who offer free, expert advice to private forest landowners. Some programs offer cost-sharing grants for thinning and fuel reduction. Supported by taxpayers, these programs are a valuable resource for the community. There are now more than 375 such programs in the U.S. which can be found by searching online for a "Resource Conservation and Development Program." In my community the Bitterroot Resource Conservation and Development Program and the State's Cooperative Extension Service have been advising private landowners for the past few decades.

Larch forests require considerable help from all parties to bring about their restoration, but the benefits of larch restoration, of course, are innumerable. Larch offers beauty, scenery, and simple enjoyment by campers, hikers, and people traversing the northwestern mountains. Larch is unique in its genetics, offering remarkable and fascinating ecology to study. Larch are an important feature and habitat for wildlife. Essentially, everyone who appreciates the Inland Northwest's Forest benefits from larch restoration.

CHAPTER FIVE

Conclusion

"Each fall (these) trees outshine all other conifers with a short-lived burst of gold-hued beauty."

BECKY KRAMER

The Spokesman-Review

Thank you for choosing to read this book and educate yourself a little bit more on Northwestern larch species. Those of us who live in the northwestern U.S. and visitors to the area may appreciate the region's massive area of accessible native forests just a little bit more, knowing that such unique and beautiful trees are a part of our forests' heritage.

I would like to encourage you to continue to learn more about larch, natural forests, and local conservation work. You might consider spending more time at National Forest and National Park visitors' centers or visiting your local chapter of National Audubon Society meetings, native plant societies, and conservation organizational meetings. Other great places to learn are the Rocky Mountain Elk Foundation in Missoula, natural history museums, and even sporting goods stores, like Cabela's or Scheels.

Of course, I would also encourage you to get out and see larch for yourself. I have lived in the Bitterroot valley in Montana since 1965 and I have hiked its recreation sites extensively. I never get tired of going to see certain stands, which over time, have become very special to me. In the preface, I mentioned going to Carlton Ridge in 1965 and seeing the alpine larch in full color in the powdery snow. What I did not mention is that my wife Bonnie and I would re-visit Carlton Ridge to see the alpine larch turn color annually for the next 54 years. I included the section "Hiking Guide to Larch in the Bitterroot" for people who are passionate about trees and who are willing and able to put in some effort to see these wonderful giants.

I would also encourage you to take others along with you to these hikes, to share your interest, enthusiasm, and appreciation for larch with a friend or family member. From my perspective, it is very important that families pass on knowledge and appreciation of a forest's heritage. Fewer people choose to recreate outdoors, and even fewer choose to spend time in the "great outdoors." Although tens of millions of people visit the Northwest's National Parks and National Forests and bring their children, I suspect very few take the time to understand or appreciate the history of those forests. For this reason, I am very encouraged that you are someone who has an interest in our natural forests, and I encourage you to find ways to pass on that interest and appreciation with others.

Acknowledgements

First, I am so grateful for those who helped with my initial research on alpine larch so many years ago. My major professor, Jim Habeck, went out of his way to help in my Ph.D. study, and my colleagues and Denny Simmerman and Mick Harrington deserve a lot of credit as well. Before and after he retired, Denny has helped me greatly in solving computer problems, including the PowerPoint program used for images in this book. Mick helped design and do the hard work of conducting studies of western larch that he continued after I retired. My field assistants Helen Smith and Micha Krebs were very helpful in our studies of western larch.

As for the manuscript itself, I had so many helpers with this manuscript that I am certain to miss naming some of them. I am deeply grateful for retired Washington State University Extension Emeritus Don Hanley for his encouragement and information that helped develop this book, as well as Penny Morgan, retired fire science teacher at the University of Idaho offered helpful comments and research publications.

I am also extremely thankful for the following people who provided photos and information for this book, including; Retired Seeley Lake Ranger District employees Tim Love and Bev Yelcyn, the Seeley Lake Historical Museum, Darris Flanagan, the Bonner School Library, the University of Montana

Archives, Allen Chrisman and family, Kevin Gedling and Stephen Mills, Peter Achuff, Randy Moody, my sons Matthew and Nathan Arno, Aaron Klug.

I am grateful for my grandson Alex, who did an outstanding job of inserting the photos in my possession and of obtaining non-copyrighted photos into the manuscript. Alex's wife, Jenny-lin Smith did a superb job of workshopping and editing the manuscript.

Larch Seeds, Trees, and Landscaping

Larch seeds and small trees available for sale

Seeds of many species of larch and hybrids are listed on ebay.com. Western larch is available from Treeseeds.com. Western larch seedlings are available to forest landowners in Washington, Oregon, Idaho, and western Montana. Contact information can be obtained from Extension Forestry offices in each state. They are available in British Columbia by contacting the provincial tree seed center at https://www2.gov.bc.ca/gov/content/industry/forestry/managing-our-forest-resources.

Alpine larch seeds and seedlings seem unavailable, and one larch supplier mentions that this species seldom survives even in northern climates where people live, echoing the findings in forestry research.

Western larch for landscaping

Portland Nursery (https://portlandnursery.com/) and Lowes.com shows images of many larches (especially weeping hybrids) they can ship for landscaping. Ordinary western larch grows far too fast for landscaping purposes. A variety of the world's larches and hybrids can be seen at Coram Experimental Forest near the Hungry Horse Ranger Station, Flathead National Forest, in NW Montana. https://www.fs.usda.gov/coreamexperimentalforest

Visitor's Guide to Northwestern Larch

Here is a list of relatively accessible areas to see larch trees in northwestern United States and southern Canada.

ALBERTA

- ALPINE LARCH: In Alberta, the trail to Larch Valley from the parking lot at 6,200-foot Moraine Lake in Banff National Park is one of several places to enjoy alpine larch trees. Another is at 7,200-foot Highwood Pass on the "Trunk Road," south of Banff.

- TAMARACK: In our region the best places to see tamarack are along the highway leading east of Alberta's Jasper National Park toward Hinton, Edson, and Edmonton and along the highway connecting Calgary and Edmonton.

BRITISH COLUMBIA

- WESTERN LARCH: British Columbia's finest western larch stands appear at Cranbrook, Kimberley, and Kamloops.

- ALPINE LARCH: British Columbia's Manning Provincial Park, east of Vancouver has several trails that thread through beautiful alpine larch stands.

OREGON

- WESTERN LARCH: The Elkhorn Scenic Loop, West of US 30, in Oregon's Blue Mountains winds in and out of big larch stands.

IDAHO

- ALPINE LARCH: Idaho has more difficult road-accessible alpine larch at Walton Lakes south of Lolo Pass and Salmon Mountain between Darby, Montana, and Elk City, Idaho.
- WESTERN LARCH: Idaho has fine groves of western larch scattered along roads and highways all the way from Moscow to Bonners Ferry.

MONTANA

- WESTERN LARCH: Seeley Lake, Montana is the most outstanding place to see big old western larch trees, including the world's largest-known larch. Many campgrounds and scenic drives among the giants (Fig. 42).
- ALPINE LARCH: Montana's most easy-to-reach alpine larch stands include those at Baker Lake up the West Fork Bitterroot Highway and St. Mary Peak, west of Stevensville. Both these hiking trails are enormously popular.

WASHINGTON

- WESTERN LARCH: The highway leading east from Mount Rainier National Park has some giant old larch as well. State Route 20 between Colville and Republic, Washington, is famed for its extensive larch stands on Sherman Pass.

- ALPINE LARCH: Perhaps the best place to visit alpine larch stands is the auto-accessible 6,100-foot Hart's Pass Recreation Area in Washington's North Cascades.

Fig. 42 Western larch line Highway 83, north of Seeley Lake (Arno)

Hiking Guide to Larch in the Bitterroot

I've put these hiking notes together for those readers would like to have a bit more context (ecological, historical, etc.) while they hike in the Bitterroot National Forest. The level of detail for each area varies, but in most of the areas described below, I include directions on how to get to the trailhead, mention great places to each lunch or check out various viewpoints, note any interesting vegetation to observe along the trail, and should I have some familiarity, I may share a bit about the history of that place. For example, whether a certain area had a fire recently.

Before you head out, I would encourage you to purchase a topographic map which contain excellent detail of roads and trails through western Montana. These maps are available from the Missoula Ranger District Office at Fort Missoula for ten dollars. Avid hikers and explorers will find these types of resources worth it. You may also consider bringing along bear spray, as bears are common in the Bitterroot Valley. Most of them are black bears and easily spooked by humans, but it never hurts to be prepared. One final note is that some of these hikes are very popular amongst locals, so it's best to get on the road early so that you can be sure to get a parking space.

A list of the different areas described appears on the next page. I hope you enjoy these areas and grow to appreciate these areas as I have. Happy trails!

Table 2. Hiking Guide to Larch in the Bitterroot		
State	**Area**	**Page**
Montana	Rattlesnake Recreation Area	106
Idaho	Tom Beal Park and Grave Peak	107
Montana	Mary's Pond	109
Montana	Lolo Recreation Area	110
Montana	Sweeney Peak	114
Montana	Bass Creek	116
Montana	St. Mary's Peak	119
Montana	Bear Creek	122
Montana	Trapper Peak	124
Montana	Medicine Point Lookout	126
Idaho	Allan Lake	128

Rattlesnake Recreation Area, Missoula

(Directions to the Thousand-Year-Old Western Larch)

There is an ancient, hollow, "living snag" more than six feet in diameter located on the Rattlesnake Creek floodplain, north of Missoula. (Fig. 43). It is quite a sight. When I first saw the tree, its base was so heavily packed with driftwood, that I had to summon help from grandson Alex (pictured) to clear the mess away.

Here are some directions to visit that thousand-

Fig. 43 A thousand-year-old western larch in the Rattlesnake Recreation Area (Arno)

year-old western larch tree. Start at the main Rattlesnake Trailhead and walk about five miles along the trail. Look for a short old telephone pole on the left. (Back in the early 1900s, a few homesteaders tried to scratch a living out of the gravelly soil, and there was phone service.) The pole may have fallen, but it is opposite the larch tree. Head directly toward the rushing water. You will wander through ten-foot-high willows, and wade through or find logs crossing the minor channels. The tree shows up close to the main channel.

Tom Beal Park/Grave Peak (Powell, Idaho)

One place to easily see alpine larch at close range is by taking the 1.5-hour-long drive that branches off from Elk Summit Road (National Forest Road 111), that starts about 10 miles west of Lolo Pass in Idaho on U.S. 12. The primitive Forest Road 362 quickly branches off to the right and leads to the Walton Lakes Trailhead (~ 46.42 N, 114.730 W). Some signs read "Tom Beal Park", which is on the same road. Along the way, you will be able to see western larch mixed in with other conifers, as well as some old, large trees. The Walton Lakes trail starts atop a broad ridge at 7,000 feet elevation and it is reached by turning left immediately before the road descends steeply into Tom Beal Park. Alpine larch grow close by in the bedrock and boulders on the steep east side of the ridge, and it is easy to follow an impromptu trail that ascends through red mountain heath and a delightful array of flowers to the 8,000-foot northern stretch of the short Grave Peak range.

Another quarter mile of hiking along this mostly smooth ridge affords views of cup-shaped basins containing small lakes and alpine larch. With binoculars, the 1924-vintage 12-by-12-foot cupola fire lookout comes into view perched atop Grave Peak's 8,282-foot precipitous summit (46.3952 N, 114.7304 W). Following the ridge farther south to the peak involves tedious technical climbing along a jagged rock backbone, but there is a six-mile-long trail leading directly to Grave Peak from the south.

That trailhead branches to the right near the end of the Elk Summit Road (Forest Road 360). It is at the end of the short spur road National Forest Road 358 leading to Kooskooskia Meadows. Beware of mosquitoes! Five miles up after a long steep and rocky stretch, the trail emerges onto a broad ridge at Friday Pass in a beautiful stand of alpine larch mixed with meadow, and a closer view of Grave Peak and its tiny lookout house (Fig.44). The last mile of trail to the lookout is narrow and was etched out of a steep rock face in the early 1900s. It is not well suited for those who fear heights, but the five-mile hike to a "top of the world view" at Friday Pass seems worth the effort, provided hikers pack bug spray. This vast country and its history are described in Bud Moore's book, *The Lochsa Story* (1996).

Fig. 44 Grave Peak Lookout (Photographer unknown)

Mary's Pond (Lolo, MT)

The un-burned larch-subalpine fir forest bordering the north side of Mary's Pond off U.S. 12 west of Lolo has tall western larch standing amid a wall of short subalpine firs (Fig. 45). Inspection showed that the larch had survived several fireswhile the firs had regenerated after the most recent one, possibly in 1889.

Fig. 45 Multi fire-scarred western larch with younger post-fire evergreens at Mary's Pond (Arno)

Lolo Peak Area (Lolo, MT)

In the Bitterroot Range, south of Missoula, the northernmost place to see alpine larch is the Lolo Peak area. Lolo is about nine miles south of Missoula on heavily trafficked US. 93. The popular trail to Carlton Lake, with a view of the north slope of One-Horse Ridge and Lolo Peak (9,096-ft.) (Fig. 46), is a good place to see alpine larch. To get to the trail, start heading south on Highway 93. Take a right on Highway 12, going towards Lolo pass. After the convenience store, you will spot Forest Service Road 612 on the left. Drive ten miles up Forest Service Road, which will take you to the Mormon Saddle (5,850 ft.) trailhead.

Fig. 46 Alpine larch beneath Lolo Peak (Arno)

The first two miles of the trail goes through the remains of a forest torched by the 2017 Lolo Peak wildfire which burned through dead, fallen lodgepole pine (*Pinus contorta*) and subalpine fir. By 2020, three-foot tall fireweed (*Epilobium angustifolium*) and lodgepole pine seedlings were the main species that regenerated after the fire. Most of the few western larch and the hybrid larch near the start of the trail were killed, both which were formerly an important feature of the Carlton Ridge Research Natural Area.

After the first two miles, the trail comes to a switchback heading south. There is a good-size stream immediately west of the switchback that is noisy and hidden by a dense growth of two-foot-tall Labrador tea (*Ledum glandulosum*). This is the best place to collect drinking water. Other streams that cross the trail are dirty and may have hundreds of hiker footsteps passing through them. The hidden creek has a braided channel that protected spruce and subalpine fir from burning.

Continue down the main trail until you come to the switchback. After the switchback you will be hiking in the burned trees. Roughly three-quarters of a mile later, at about 7,200 feet, the trail recrosses the stream, and you will finally be able to see a handful of surviving alpine larch. (There were not many there before the fire either). Then you hike again through burned forest, which contained whitebark pine and lodgepole. After gaining a few hundred feet of elevation, the north-heading trail enters another open, north-facing stand of surviving alpine larch.

Along this stretch, look for a mountain hemlock growing on the upper side of the trail. Mountain hemlocks are normally confined to moderately high mountains in Idaho, far northwestern Montana north of Lolo Pass, and in the Pacific Northwest. Around 7,200 feet, the trail threads through a patchwork of burned and unburned trees. When you are around 8,000-feet in elevation, the trail passes through a younger stand of whitebark pine and larch, many of which survived the fire. You may be able to see cones atop the whitebark pines. The multi-species forest on the left is burned, and in a short distance, at the west end of Carlton Ridge, the trail leads to the good viewpoint of the larch covering the north face of Lolo Peak (which is unburned), its basin, Carlton Lake, and the larch-surrounded marsh that is above Carlton Lake (Fig. 47).

Fig. 47 Alpine larch around marsh near Carlton Lake, MT
(Photographer unknown)

By mid-summer, Carlton Lake Reservoir is usually drained and has a border of mud because it is not maintained well. If you walk south, across the dam, you will enter a magnificent forest of big, old-growth alpine larch mixed with tall spruce, subalpine fir, whitebark pines, and a luxuriant undergrowth of red mountain heath (*Cassiope metensiana*), smooth woodrush (*Luzula glabrata*), grouse whortleberry (*Vaccinium scoparium*), and assorted flowers, including marsh marigold (*Caltha leptosepala*). This assemblage fills the moist basin leading to the 8,200-foot pass separating One-Horse Ridge and the Lolo Peak mastiff.

Climbing west by southwest through the talus from the west end of the Carlton Reservoir leads to an interesting 8,450-foot elevation krummholz saddle where the evergreen trees are reduced to low cushions. Alpine larch has both a cushion of ground-hugging branches and erect flags sticking up as much as eight feet high (Fig. 48).

Fig. 48 Krummholz alpine larch. Larch on Lolo Peak, MT (Arno)

Sweeney Peak (Florence, MT)

Sweeney Peak (9,167-ft.) on the Bitterroot National Forest is barely visible from the Lolo Peak viewpoint. It provides an excellent opportunity to hike through alpine larch stands and see old living western larch along the lower part of the trail.

The Sweeney Ridge trailhead is reached by turning west off the Sweeney Creek Road, about two miles south of Florence, Montana. About a mile up the road, there is a cattle guard. Then, the gravel National Forest Road 1315 leads to Sweeney Ridge Trail (5,800 ft.), whose main attractions are Peterson, Duffy, and Holloway Lakes. The last half-mile of the Road 1315 is extremely steep, narrow, and often covered with loose gravel, so it is best to use a four-wheel-drive vehicle with high clearance. The parking area is quite small for such a popular trail, so it is a good idea to arrive early in the morning and to back your vehicle in, since it is difficult to turn around. Visitors will notice that fire underburned the forest along the upper part of the road. This was a fuels management project conducted by the Stevensville Ranger District of the U. S. Forest Service.

At about 6,000 ft. on the Ridge Crest trail , there is a good viewpoint immediately to the south. You will be able to see alpine larch on the north side of the ridge between Sweeney and Bass Creeks. You will also be able to see the steep, shallow cirque on the northeastern face of St. Joseph Peak (9,537 ft.), the highest mountain in the northern Bitterroot Range. A short way farther along the trail, you will see a "wolfy" old Douglas-fir, which is about five feet thick and has great, big limbs that go all the way to the ground. Then, the trail passes through old-growth Douglas-fir and mostly beetle-killed ponderosa pines. Roughly one mile after the old-growth Douglas-fir and ponderosa pine section (and about one and a half miles from the trailhead), there is a rocky outcrop viewpoint with a better view of St. Joseph Peak.

To reach Sweeney Peak, head west on Sweeney Ridge trail. About a mile from the rocky outcrop viewpoint, you will see a marshy waterhole immediately below the trail. This is the take-off point for climbing Sweeney Peak. There is no trail per se, so it is cross-country from here. You will need to go west, finding your own route through a broad saddle that separates Sweeney Ridge from the peak. You will wade through small Labrador tea-covered wetlands in the saddle, and then continue trying to find the best route west through fallen trees beyond the saddle.

At some point, your route should reach the sharp spine leading to Sweeney Peak Ridge. There will be a good view of the small basin on the north side of the ridge. After a steep climb to the 8,500-foot level, hikers come to a flat, open grove of small alpine larch . These trees short, even for alpine larch apparently due to poor soil. Directly ahead, still going west along the spine of Sweeney Peak Ridge, you encounter loose talus (big boulders) which you will need to cross. Be careful, the rocks may shift under your weight. A steep climb up the spine will get you close to the summit ridge. You will be able to see the northeast face of Sweeney Peak and views of the Peterson, Duffy, and Holloway Lakes. When the ridge ends, you will have reached a relatively flat, long summit block. If there is a strong westerly wind, hikers can huddle in the whitebark pine krummholz on the north side of the crest. It's a good place to eat lunch, because it's still quite a way along the wind-exposed crest to reach the summit.

The summit is marked by an iron pipe and U.S. Geological Survey brass cap. From here, hikers can see the big cirque at the head of One-Horse Creek, which contains lakes and ponds. You can also see the two summits of Lolo Peak, the rounded one at about 9,130-feet, and the sharper summit at about 9,096 feet. Other high peaks to the southwest appear, along with Idaho's Grave Peak range, and the seemingly endless rounded ridges of the Selway-Bitterroot Wilderness Area. Duffy Lake is a seldom visited gem, perched just below a high divide, and surrounded by alpine larch.

Bass Creek Recreation Area (Stevensville, MT)

Continuing south down the Bitterroot, the next location gives visitors a chance to see both western and alpine larch in the same area. Head south on highway 93 and take the road labelled Bass Creek Recreation Area. In early October, you will be able to see alpine larch turning color high up on the broad ridge and western larch just starting to turn color on the lower slopes, even from the road (Fig. 49).

Fig. 49 Alpine larch growing in snow on Little St. Joseph Peak and western larch below (Dennis Simmerman)

To get to the Bass Creek Overlook (and climb the trail that leads to the alpine larch you saw from near the highway), turn right at the Bass Creek trailhead's parking area, and follow Road 1136. It gains a few thousand feet of elevation to reach the small parking area (6,100 ft. elevation) at road's end. At times, there's been a picnic table at the brink of the overlook, where there is a great view of the colorful Kootenai Crags.

From the Bass Creek Overlook, you can get to the trail leading to 9,350-foot Little St. Joe (9,350 ft.), and ultimately the difficult climb of St. Joseph Peak (9,537 ft.), head west from the parking lot. The trail to little St. Joe ends at another viewpoint of alpine larch growing on loose talus. There is a great lunch stop at about 7,500 feet, where sometimes you can see the informal ski area immediately to the north, and sometimes skiers. Climb straight up through the steep, talus slope, covered with an open stand of alpine larch, spruce, subalpine fir, and mostly beetle-killed whitebark pines. Subalpine firs often use open-grown alpine larch with big spreading limbs as a trellis; the subalpine firs grow up through the gaps between the alpine larch branches and lean against alpine larch (Fig. 50). The larch protects the firs weak stems.

At about 8,000 feet elevation, you will be able to see the ski area better. There is an open area in the middle of the broad, east-facing ridge, which experienced skiers use in late May and

Fig. 50 Subalpine Fir Using Alpine Larch as a Trellis (Arno)

June. Just a little higher, at about 8,500 ft., there's an area of krummholz which is a good place to eat lunch and see terrific views, of the Bitterroot Range, Bitterroot Valley, and the Sapphire Range, to the east. Near the 9,000-foot elevation, hikers may see a few remains of the firefighting tanker that crashed on a foggy October day in 1991. Tragically, the pilot and co-pilot died in the crash and the big aerial tanker's wreckage was strewn all over the area until the Forest Service (and probably its owner, Johnson's Flying Service) managed to clear out most of it.

The view from Little St. Joe's 9,350 ft summit takes in much of the Bitterroot Valley with towns and extensive developed areas. You'll be able to see Kent Peak (9,000 ft.), the highest one in the Sapphire Range. Immediately south, you will be able to see a mountain with a lookout house that equals the height of Little St. Joe. That mountain is another place to see a variety of both western and alpine larch trees. It is the enormously popular St. Mary Peak.

St. Mary Peak (Stevensville, MT)

The people of Stevensville calls St. Mary's Peak "Stevensville's Mountain." Stevensville, the first town in Montana, is named in honor of Washington Territorial Governor Isaac Stevens and was established as a mission by Jesuit Father Pierre De Smet in 1841. The original log church is still maintained and used for special occasions. By the way, in the 1850s Montana west of the Continental Divide was initially part of both Washington and Oregon Territories, and then briefly part of Idaho Territory, before becoming Montana Territory in 1864.

Visitors can reach St. Mary Peak (9,351ft.) by taking Forest Road 739 off St. Mary's Road that heads west, about two miles south of Stevensville Junction on Highway 93. Forest Road 739 is long and full of switchbacks. It travels through western larch trees, including old ones, snags, vigorous young trees, and on old logging sites before finally reaching the trailhead parking lot and privy at 7,000 feet. This is an enormously popular trail, so it is best to arrive in early morning.

Start hiking the main trail. At the fourth switchback look for the old haggard mountain hemlock, just off the hiking trail to the south. It has suffered frost damage many times because this species is adapted to living in a moist, snowy environment, and sub-zero temperatures often occur here when there is little or no snow to cover the trees. A small spring and waterhole surrounded by Labrador tea appears about one mile beyond the trailhead. Its water needs to be filtered before drinking.

From the waterhole, the trail continues climbing. It passes through lodgepole pine and big dead whitebark pines (the legacy of bark-beetle attacks). Although there are also some young whitebark, many of them have tell-tale cankers of white pine blister rust (*Cronartium ribicola*). At about 8,200 feet elevation, the south-slope trail nears the ridgetop. If you climb a short way up, you can see a small alpine larch-occupied basin and St. Mary Peak's east face. About a half mile beyond this point, there will be an option for you to hike to the lakes or hike to the peak. Hikers can leave the main trail and contour southwest to find a rounded spur ridge and then the faint, old trail leading down to the fish-less (and therefore, little-used) McCalla Lakes, which are both surrounded by alpine larch. The second McCalla lake is a real beauty and I would recommend making the effort to see it.

Otherwise, the trail to the peak itself passes through a succession of whitebark pine krummholz and ultimately to cushion krummholz and alpine wildflowers. In this stretch, look near the ridge's edge on the right for signs of the former erect forest, buried in the low krummholz with dead, fallen whitebark trunks eight or more inches in diameter. What killed them? We are not entirely sure. It could have been extreme fire or bark beetles, or something else, but we are not one hundred percent sure. Occasionally an alpine larch krummholz with a tall flag sticking up appears along the way. Around the summit, there are even three Douglas-fir cushion krummholz. "Doug fir", as foresters call it, is the most widespread of all forest plants in the inland West. They normally do not grow at 9,000 ft. elevation, so it is unusual to see them here.

The view from the mountain's summit is breathtaking. Be sure to see the Heavenly Twins peaks to the west and a sheer, 1,500 foot drop off to the U-shaped, alpine larch-dominated gorge called Larch Canyon.

Bear Creek (Victor, MT)

Bear Creek Trail starts off Forest Road 738, opposite Bell Crossing on Highway 93, is a thoroughfare with dead and dying larch lining it (Fig. 51). The first few miles has these dead and dying larch, which are overcrowded by pacific yew (*Taxus brevifolia*), subalpine fir, grand fir, Douglas fir, and spruce. But then some good-looking western larch starting about six miles up it.

Fig. 51 Dying western larch and ponderosa pines along Bear Creek (Arno)

What might have happened here? Looking closely, you will see fire scars on old growth larch and ponderosa pines, revealing that prior to 1900, the canyon bottom burned two to three times per century. This favored western larch and ponderosa pine, while checking encroachment by spruce, subalpine pine, grand fir, and the nearly impenetrable layer of ten-foot-high Pacific yew that covers the riparian area. Big ponderosa pine trees are dead or dying from root and trunk rot or bark beetles. Nearly all the old larch trees died from competitive exclusion, combined with dwarf mistletoe infection. There is no chance for larch or ponderosa to regenerate until a wildfire guts the canyon, which inevitably will happen sometime. The mouth of Big Creek is far too close to the wildland-urban interface for the Forest Service to risk burning. It is not clear why the upper canyon's western larch looked good on my last visit in 2008, but they did not have the level of competition seen near the canyon's mouth.

The Bear Overlook Trailhead is located west of Victor, Montana, at the end of Forest Road 1325. In October, after a two and a half-mile climb from the 6,000-ft. elevation trailhead to the 7,000-ft. overlook, visitors can see a large basin full of brilliant western larch. It is not clear why these western larch trees seem to be thriving when again the ones near Bear Creek's mouth are dying from the effects of insects, disease, excessive competition, and lack of fire. The short trail to a gorgeous viewpoint is very popular, and the parking area at road's end is small. Bear Creek Overlook sits atop a sheer cliff, so viewers should be wary. When the trail was first built, my family used to watch white, shaggy mountain goats laying on the ledges beneath it, but hunters and poachers have done away with them. Most of those shot probably were not retrievable.

A flourishing plantation of young western larch trees about 25 miles south of its natural distribution can be seen along Forest Road 3201 just south of the trailhead for Little Rock Creek Lakes. This one and others south of its range make clear that the tree can grow well over a broader area than it occupies.

Trapper Peak (Darby, MT)

South along the west side of the Bitterroot Range, a location no tree enthusiast should miss, is the hike up to 10,157-foot Trapper Peak. The trail takes off from Forest Road 617 located a few miles up the West Fork Highway beyond the Trapper Creek Job Corps Center. After the road ends at the 5,800-foot level, you will begin a long slog up through the south-facing forest. As it passes the 7,500-foot level, there is a gradual change from lodgepole pine and subalpine fir to whitebark pine with fir, spruce and scattered alpine larch. By the 8,500-foot mark, lodgepole is mostly replaced by whitebark pine, and damp areas support alpine larch. On the west side, larch meadows appear with big, spreading trees (Fig. 52). As you continue, there are ever more alpine larch along the rocky surface and fewer evergreens. By the 9,500-foot level, it's almost exclusively alpine larch ten to twelve feet tall. They show little sign of the battering they endure in winter and nearly all the scattered krummholz cushions on the talus-clad summit block is alpine larch.

Fig. 52 Spreading alpine larch on Trapper Peak (Arno)

An awe-inspiring rock glacier lays half a vertical mile below the summit of 10,157-foot Trapper Peak southwest of Darby, Montana. Carefully peering over this formidable precipice reveals aquamarine Cave Lake which is colored greenish by glacial "rock flour" (Fig. 53). Alpine larch colonizes the moraine that dams Cave Lake. Rock glaciers receive massive amounts of snow when blizzards scour the exposed south slopes and summits and blow the snow over the cliffs. Huge snow cornices form each winter on the summits and hang over the headwall. They provide another source of snow and frigid water that turns into ice, which start to form the core of a new rock glacier.

Fig. 53 Rock glacier and Cave Lake near summit of Trapper Peak
(Google Earth photo, obtained by Nathan Arno)

Years ago, I was walking atop one of these cornices, several feet back from its edge, when I heard and felt a sudden crack followed by a thunderous rumble right behind me. The cornice gave way along my path, plunging 1,500 feet down. I scurried far from its edge instantly and had one heck of an adrenaline rush!

Medicine Point Lookout (Conner, MT)

There are still two more places worth visiting to see alpine larch in the Bitterroot Range. At 8,409 feet, with Medicine Point Lookout being as far south as it is, it might not be expected to harbor a grove of alpine larch. Now I know from experience to check out the steep north-facing slope. Sure enough, there is a small grove of larch there at the end of the four-mile-long trail to the peak! Another even more unusual feature of Medicine Point is the narrow ridgetop ribbon forest, immediately to the north.

Unfortunately, it burned in a wildfire several years ago. Artist Ramona Hammerly sketched a ribbon forest, and I described how they're formed in our book, *Timberline: Mountain and Arctic Forest Frontiers*, published in 1984 by Mountaineers Books.

There isn't any larch on this trail except on Medicine Point itself. The trail starts at the Laird Creek turnoff from U.S. 93, several miles south of Darby, Montana. At first, the route follows Forest Road 8758, and then is near the 6,500-foot trailhead Road 8759. An ample parking area is located at the road's end, and the trail gets only moderate use. It is a rather easy hike and well worth it even for people not interested in trees.

Incidentally, the lower Laird Creek Drainage burned in a 2000 wildfire. The Forest Service hired helicopters at about $2,000 per hour at taxpayer expense to drop water on the houses. It worked in the lower drainage, but not as much farther up. There were more at-risk houses up nearby Warm Springs Creek. It was there that we talked to a man whose summer retreat was saved, but he said he would rather the buildings had burned than the beautiful forest around it. He also had quite a bit of work to do to clean up the area. He would have to hire crews to clear out the big, charred trees around his property. They would most likely be burned in piles. New trees would be replanted, he would need to restore the lawn, as well as utility lines. I have heard this tale of woe repeatedly.

Allan Lake (Lemhi County, Idaho)

Although Allan Lake should be listed in Idaho's places worth seeing, I have visited it from Montana. This lake is in Idaho's part of the Bitterroot Range, but it can be reached from two directions. Allan Lake is surrounded by alpine larch. There was good fishing when I was there. It's talus-ringed and about 7,700 feet in elevation. The lake is about a seven-mile hike from the trailhead and worth visiting. For those driving south on U.S. 93 over Lost Trail Pass, the best access road turns off right, 14 miles from the Pass at Twin Creek Campground, and follows Forest Road 115, until it joins Road 89. For people travelling north from Salmon and North Fork, Idaho, access is 26 miles north of Salmon, less than a mile before Gibbonsville, and turning left on Forest Road 92 and then tying into Road 89.

I've reached it from Montana by a mostly cross-country route. If you'd like to try it, drive up toward Painted Rocks Reservoir and then proceed to Alta. Turn left, up the Hughes Creek Road, just past Than Wilkerson's historic ranger station. Follow this road several miles, then turn right on Road 5688 and drive about a mile past the ponds on your left. At that point, you can cross Mine Creek and climb the gentle-sloping spur ridge that leads to the Interstate-Boundary trail. Follow it northeast, left, a little over a mile until you come to the second trail on your right. That's number 112, which soon reaches the rim above Allan Lake and looks across at 9,154-foot Allan Mountain.

Recommendations for Further Reading

The following are a few of the many publications dealing with research and findings related to western larch, alpine larch, other larch species, and hybrids.

- Alpine larch research is being conducted in the **Carlton Ridge Research Natural Area**, Lolo National Forest, Montana, where the 2017 Lolo Peak wildfire burned with unprecedented severity and killed much of the larch, but patches of seedlings have appeared. Studies will produce results of larch recovery after wildfire.

- Hybridization of alpine and western larch where the two mix on talus and form typical as well as various intermediate forms is published in *Natural Areas Journal* (1990), op. cit. The authors of this publication determined that hybrids occur and give criteria for identification of them.

- "Ecology of alpine larch," *Ecological Monographs*. (1972), op. cit., gives detailed information and description of the species throughout its very scattered range. This is the only publication that gives detailed information about alpine larch throughout its range.

- **"Forest Habitat Types of Montana**," Pfister, R. et. al., 1977. USDA Forest Service General Technical Report INT-34 characterizes pure and mixed-species alpine larch habitats.

- **"Cone and Seed Morphology of Western Larch, Alpine Larch and their Hybrids,"** Carlson, C. and L. Theroux, 1993. Canadian Journal of Forest Research 23:1264-1269 compares cone and seed morphology among the two larch species and hybrids.

- **"Germination and Early Growth of Western Larch, Alpine Larch and their Reciprocal Hybrids,"** Carlson, C., 1994. Canadian Journal of Forest Research 24:911-916. Alpine larch trees were used in experimental cross-pollination with western larch from another area. Hybrid seedlings produced appeared robust and may be useful and may be useful in revegetating sites marginally too cold for western larch.

- **"Ecology and Management of Larix Forests,"** USDA Forest Service, General Technical Report INT-319 (1995), available by contacting the publications office at the Rocky Mountain Station, Fort Collins, CO. (970) 498 1100, it includes many papers explaining research projects dealing with western and alpine larch, and many other larch species and hybrids, and provides results.

- **"Old-Growth Ponderosa Pine and Western Larch Stand Structures: Influences of Pre-1900 Fires and Fire Exclusion,"** (1997), op. cit. Western larch fire scars and fire initiated larch age-classes were used in conjunction with archeological evidence and historical accounts to indicate that the frequent firesin a moist, frosty larch-dominated valley resulted from Native American burning.

- **"Fire-Climate-Vegetation Interactions in Subalpine Forests of the Selway-Bitterroot Wilderness Area, Idaho and Montana"**, USA, Kipfmueller, K., 2003. Ph.D. Dissertation, University of Arizona, Tucson. Alpine larch growth-ring sequences were used to develop a 748-year chronology. This and other studies have found alpine larch growth rings sensitive to climatic changes.

- **"Reconstructing Annual Area Burned in the Northern Rockies, USA,"** Knapp, P., and P. Soule, 2011. *Geophysical Research Letters* 38:17402. Growth-ring sequences from alpine larch from 1626 to 2008 were successfully used as an index of annual area burned. Results suggest that the period 1929-1945 would have been the most active since the early 1600s had not fire suppression and logging altered the fire regime.

References

The following books, articles, journals, and websites provided background and informed our research. While we have taken precautions to ensure that the content of this book is accurate and up to date, it is impossible to include all sources because of the very broad scope of subjects presented and the fact that we consulted a variety of online sources.

INTRODUCTION

Wythe, L. (n.d.). *Western Larch / Tamarack*. Kinnikinic Native Plant Society. http://nativeplantsociety.org/western-larch.

CHAPTER 1

Arno, S. Personal observations.

Arno, S., 1970, Ecology of alpine larch [Larix lyallii Parl.].} in the Pacific Northwest, Ph.D. Dissertation, University of Montana, Missoula, 432 p.

Carlson, C., 1995, Natural hybrids of western and alpine larch, Ecology and management of Larix Forests: a look ahead, USDA Forest Service, General Technical Report INT-319:473-474.

Eckenwalder, J., 2009, Conifers of the world, Timber Press, Portland, OR.

Johnson, W., 1990, Larix laricina [tamarack], pp. 141-151 in: Silvics of North America, Vol.1, Conifers, USDA Forest Service, Washington, DC

Little, E. L., 1971. Atlas of United States Trees, Vol. 1. USDA Forest Service, Misc. Publication 1146.

Richards, J. and L. Bliss, 1986, Winter water relations of a deciduous timberline conifer, Larix lyallii Parl. *Oecologia* 69: 16-24

Waring, R. and J. Franklin, 1979, Evergreen coniferous forests of the Pacific Northwest, Science 204:1380-1386

Wilson, C, 2001, Regeneration dynamics of Larix lyallii in forests of the southern Canadian Rockies, Ph.D. Thesis, Department of Biological Sciences, University of Alberta, Edmonton.

CHAPTER 2

Arno, S., October 1969 aerial reconnaissance & 2012 sighting from a high- mountain viewpoint.

Arno, S., 1970, Ecology of alpine larch [Larix lyallii Parl.].} in the Pacific Northwest, Ph.D. Dissertation, University of Montana, Missoula, 78 p.

Arno, S. and J. Habeck, 1972, Ecology of alpine larch [*Larix lyallii* Parl.] in the Pacific Northwest, Ecological Monographs. 42:417-450, p. 424

Arno, S. and J. Habeck, 1972, Ecology of alpine larch [*Larix lyallii* Parl.] in the Pacific Northwest, Ecological Monographs. 42:417-450, p. 448

Beckey, F., 1981. *Cascade Alpine Guide [no. 3], Rainy Pass to Fraser River*, The Mountaineers –Books, 80 p.

Eckenwalder, J. 2009. Op.cit.

Hanley, Don, 2020. Emeritus Head of Washington's Extension Forestry Department provided this information.

Johnson, W., 1990, Larix laricina [tamarack], pp. 141-151 in: Silvics of North America, Vol.1, Conifers, USDA Forest Service, Washington, D. C.

Leiberg, J., 1900, U.S. Geological Survey, 20th Annual Report, Part Five, 336 p.

Little, E. 1971. Op. cit.

Lyn Topinka, 2012. *The Columbia River - Bridal Veil, Oregon*, http://columbiariverimages.com/Regions/Places/bridal_veil_lumbering_company.html.

Montana Magazine, September/October 2005, Helena, Montana; and available on-line.

Sargent, C., 1884. *Forests of North America*, U.S. Census Office.

Townsend, E. 2019. Is Hybrid Larch the Future of the Northern Forest? The Forestry Source 24 (12): 1, 10-11. Society of American Foresters, Bethesda, MD.

Van Pelt, R. 2001, *Forest Giants of the Pacific Coast*, University of
    Washington Press.
Viereck, L. and E. Little Jr., 1972, Alaska trees and shrubs, USDA
    Forest Service, Agriculture Handbook 410, Washington, DC.
Wallowa-Whitman National Forest - Home,
    https://www.fs.usda.gov/wallowa-whitman.

CHAPTER 3

Arno, S. Personal observation, July 1969.
Arno and Habeck, 1972. Op. cit.
Arno, S. F., H. Smith, and M. Krebs. Old Growth Ponderosa Pine and
    Western Larch Stand Structures: Influences of Pre-1900 Fires
    and Fire Exclusion. USDA Forest Service, Research Paper
    INT-495.
Ayres 1901: Arno et al. 1997.
Ayres, H.B.,1901. Lewis and Clark Forest Reserve, Montana. 21st
    Annual Report Part V, USDI, Geological Survey: 27-80.
Flanagan, D., 2003, Skid Trails: Glory Days of Montana Logging,
    Stoneydale Press, Stevensville, MT; Holbrook, S. 1944. Holy
    Old Mackinaw. Macmillan, N.Y.
Flanagan, D., 2003, Skid Trails: Glory Days of Montana Logging,
    Stoneydale Press, Stevensville, MT, 176 p.
Flanagan, D., 2003, Skid Trails: Glory Days of Montana Logging,
    Stoneydale Press, Stevensville, MT, p.101.
Flanagan, D., 2003, Skid Trails: Glory Days of Montana Logging,
    Stoneydale Press, Stevensville, MT, p. 103.
Gordon, G., 2014. When Money Grew on Trees. University of
    Oklahoma Press, p. 236-291.
Hanley, D., 2020. Emeritus Head of Washington's Extension Forestry
    Department provided this information.
Luckman, B. 1986. Reconstruction of Little Ice Age events in the
    Canadian Rocky Mountains, Geographic physique et
    Quaternaire 60 [1]: 17-28 [Montréal]
Munger, B. S. 1993. Whitebark pine: A prehistoric food source at
    timberline in the Bitterroot Mountains of Montana. University
    of California, Santa Barbara, CA, USA.; Munger, B. S. 1993.

High country archaeology in the Bitterroot Mountains.
Archaeology in Montana 34:1-6.

Nisbet, J.,1994. *Sources of the River: Tracking David Thompson across Western North America*. p. 114. Sasquatch Books, Seattle.

Robbins, Jim. "Chronicles of the Rings: What Trees Tell Us." *The New York Times*, The New York Times, 30 Apr. 2019, https://www.nytimes.com/2019/04/30/science/tree-rings-climate.html.

"Western Larch." *The Wood Database*, https://www.wood-database.com/western-larch/.

CHAPTER 4

Barrett, S, S. Arno, and C Key, 1991. Fire regimes of western larch-lodgepole pine forests in Glacier National Park, Montana, Canadian Journal of Forest Research 21: 1711-1720.

Kipfmueller, K. (2008). Reconstructed summer temperature in the northern Rocky Mountains wilderness, USA. *Quaternary Research*, 70(2), 173-187. doi:10.1016/j.yqres.2008.04.003

Kipfmueller, Kurt F., and Thomas W. Swetnam. "Fire-Climate Interactions in the Selway-Bitterroot Wilderness Area." *In: Cole, David N.; McCool, Stephen F.; Borrie, William T.; O'Loughlin, Jennifer, Comps. 2000. Wilderness Science in a Time of Change Conference-Volume 5: Wilderness Ecosystems, Threats, and Management; 1999 May 23–27; Missoula, MT. Proceedings RMRS-P-15-VOL-5. Ogden, UT: U.S. Department of Agriculture, Forest Service, Rocky Mountain Research Station. p. 270-275*, 1 Jan. 1970, https://www.fs.usda.gov/treesearch/pubs/21873.

"The 1910 Fires." *Forest History Society*, 9 Oct. 2020, https://foresthistory.org/research-explore/us-forest-service-history/policy-and-law/fire-u-s-forest-service/famous-fires/the-1910-fires/.

"U.S. Forest Service Fire Suppression." *Forest History Society*, 9 Apr. 2020, https://foresthistory.org/research-explore/us-forest-service-history/policy-and-law/fire-u-s-forest-service/u-s-forest-service-fire-suppression/.

Wallowa-Whitman National Forest - Home,
https://www.fs.usda.gov/wallowa-whitman.

CHAPTER 5

Kramer, B., Oct. 13,2010, Western larch trees turning gold, dropping
needles, The Spokesman- Review, Spokane, WA

"Lee Metcalf - Lee Metcalf - U.S. Fish and Wildlife Service." *U.S. Fish
& Wildlife Service,*
https://www.fws.gov/refuge/lee_metcalf/about/Lee_Metcalf.ht
ml.

"Welcome." *Whitebark Pine Ecosystem Foundation*, 12 Mar.
2019, https://whitebarkfound.org/.

Visitor's Guide to Larch in the Bitterroot

Arno, S. F. *Timberline: Mountain and Arctic Forest Frontiers*. The
Mountaineers 1984 Ib. 85.

Moore, Bud. *The Lochsa Story: Land Ethics in the Bitterroot
Mountains*. Mountain Press Pub., 1996.

Index

A

B

E

F

J

K

L

M

N

O

P

R

S

T

About the Author

STEPHEN F. ARNO devoted his career to forestry research with the U.S. Forest Service. He holds a Ph.D. in Forestry and Plant Science (University of Montana, 1970) and is considered an expert in forest ecology, fire ecology, and the application of prescribed fire and managing fuels. Although retired, he still enjoys sharing his passion for forestry with others through his writing.